A GROWI...M

Pesticides and t...

by David Bull

First published in 1982
© OXFAM 1982

ISBN 0 85598 064 8

Printed by OXFAM Print Room

Published by OXFAM,
274 Banbury Road,
Oxford, OX2 7DZ

Contents

Some notes on the terms and conventions used in this book.

The Poor
It is difficult to measure poverty and the numbers affected by it. The World Bank estimates that about 800 million people are living in what it calls "absolute poverty", and probably as many again are only a little better off. The majority live in rural areas, and the greatest concentration is in South and East Asia.

The Third World
There is no satisfactory way of describing the group of countries which contain many poor people. In this book the term 'Third World' is used as a shorthand which does at least reflect (through the use of the word 'world') the diversity of countries it encompasses. The Third World includes about a hundred countries containing some 3,000 million people.

The Researchers
The research for this book was carried out by full-time OXFAM staff — principally the author, but with assistance from colleagues in the Third World and in Oxford. The researchers are referred to as 'we' in the text.

Sources
As well as books, articles and official documents, a large number of experts have been consulted in the course of the research and their letters provide a number of the sources quoted in the references. The term 'personal communication' refers to a letter from the person quoted. The phrase 'in interview with' means that no written record exists — but that the points made in the interview have afterwards been referred back to the person interviewed.

Some of the sources quoted are OXFAM files. Anyone wishing to see any of the files referred to should write to the Overseas Director, OXFAM, 274 Banbury Road, Oxford OX2 7DZ.

OXFAM Support
OXFAM seldom provides 100% of the cost of a scheme — so where projects are described as 'OXFAM-supported' or 'OXFAM-funded', it should be remembered that most of the cost is usually paid for by the local people and/or other aid agencies.

Currencies
The sterling (£) equivalent of local currencies is given in brackets in most cases. The exchange rate used is either that in force on the date in question, or, where the date is a year, the average of end-of-month exchange rates for that year, unless otherwise specified.

Companies
Companies are referred to in the text by their short names — eg 'Velsicol' rather than the full name 'Velsicol Chemical Corporation'.

OXFAM's dialogue with the pesticide manufacturers continued after this Report was completed. It has not been possible to take into account in the text all the points made after the end of March 1982.

Acronyms
It becomes tedious to repeat the often lengthy names of organisations in full and so acronyms or initials are used. The acronym is given in brackets after the full name the first time it is mentioned, and a list of abbreviations is given in Appendix III.

Acknowledgements

I wish to extend my most sincere thanks to all those who have contributed to the completion of this book. Their contributions have included the provision of information and of helpful and constructive comments on the various drafts of the text; discussion of points of analysis; advice and moral support, and help with the physical preparation of the manuscript for publication.

I am particularly grateful to Jeff and Barbara Alderson for their hospitality during my visit to India, and to my colleagues in the Public Affairs Unit, Dianna Melrose and Adrian Moyes for their considerable help, advice and support. I would also like to extend special thanks to the staff of the Secretarial Services Department in OXFAM for their help and patience despite the frequent pressure of impossible deadlines. Many other members of staff, both in Britain and in OXFAM offices around the world, have assisted in various ways.

I wish also to express my gratitude to those members of OXFAM's Field Committees and Council who gave up their time to discuss the manuscript, especially to the Editorial Panel, under the Chairmanship of Dr. William Francis.

I am grateful to all those organisations and individuals who helped by sending out and by completing questionnaires, and also to the following:
Dr. A. Balasubramaniam (Pesticide Board, Ministry of Agriculture, Malaysia); Melot Balisalisa (Farmers' Assistance Board, Philippines); Ing Pedro Bodegas (Southeastern Centre for Ecological Research, Mexico); Dr. Lucas Brader (FAO); Shirley A. Briggs (Rachel Carson Council, US); staff of the Central Agricultural Research Institute and the Agricultural Extension Service, Sri Lanka; Graham Collins (Pesticides Branch, Ministry of Agriculture, Fisheries and Food, UK); Dr. Gordon Conway (Chiang Mai University, Thailand); Dr. J.F. Copplestone (Pesticide Development and Safe Use, WHO); Ian Craig (Imperial College Centre for Environmental Technology, UK); Anwar Fazal and colleagues (International Organisation of Consumers Unions, Malaysia); Dr. Grace Goodell (formerly of International Rice Research Institute, Philippines); Beth Goodson and colleagues (International Federation of Plantation, Agricultural and Allied Workers, Switzerland); Dr. Peter Haskell and colleagues (Centre for Overseas Pest Research, UK); Dr. K.L. Heong (Malaysian Agricultural Research and Development Institute, Malaysia); Dr. J. Jeyeratnam (formerly of Department of Community Medicine, Faculty of Medicine, Colombo, Sri Lanka); Prem Chandran John (Training & Service Centre in Community Health and Development, Deenabandu, India); Martin Kohr and colleagues (Consumers' Association of Penang, Malaysia); Dr. Graham Matthews (Overseas Spraying Machinery Centre, UK); Dr. Kenneth Mellanby; Banpot Napompeth (Director, National Biological Control Research Center, Thailand); Dr. Ravi Narayan (St John's Medical College, Bangalore, India); Dr. G.A. Norton and colleagues (Imperial College, UK); Dr. Livia Oliveira (Universidade Estadual Paulista, Brazil); N.J. Pickerin and colleagues (Pesticides Branch, Ministry of Agriculture, Fisheries and Food, UK); Dr. G.B. Pickering (Tropical Products Institute, UK); Dr. C.P. Pant and colleagues (Ecology and Control of Vectors Unit, WHO); Professor David Pimentel (Department of Entomology, Cornell University, US); Dr. Bill Reed (International Crops Research Institute for the Semi-Arid Tropics, Hyderabad, India); Dr. R.M. Sawicki (Rothamsted Experimental Station, UK); Sarvodaya Shramadana Movement, Sri Lanka; S. Jacob Scherr (Natural Resources Defense Council, US); Michael Scott (OXFAM America, US); S. Selliah (International Federation of Plantation, Agricultural and Allied Workers, India); Dr. Fred J. Simmonds (ex-Director, Commonwealth Institute for Biological Control, India); Professor Ray F. Smith (Consortium for International Crop Protection, US); Dr. Andrew Spielman (School of Public Health, Harvard University, US); Pierre Spitz (UN Research Institute for Social Development, Switzerland); Dr. Joyce Tait (Open University, UK); Tan Chai Ket (Sahabat Alam Malaysia, Malaysia); Dr. E.M. Thain (Tropical Products Institute, UK); Bill Upholt (ex-Environmental Protection Agency, US); Dr. G.K. Veeresh (University of Agricultural Sciences, Bangalore, India); Robert Wasserstrom (Department of Anthropology, Columbia University, US); Dr. John Wyon (Department of Population Sciences, Harvard University, US); Dr. David Werner (Hesperian Foundation, US), and Dr. Fred Whittemore (US Agency for International Development, US).

Many more people have given valuable assistance and their help is no less appreciated for the fact that space does not permit all their names to be listed here.

Finally I would like to thank all those representatives of the agrochemical industry who have provided help and information. These include Chris Major of the British Agrochemicals Association and staff of the following companies: Bayer, Ciba-Geigy, Cyanamid, Dow, Du Pont, FBC, FMC, Hoechst, ICI, Lankem Ceylon, Rhone-Poulenc, Sandoz, Shell, Sumitomo, Union Carbide, and Velsicol.

David Bull.

Introduction

In the dusty heat of South India, the monsoon has failed. Ten miles down a dirt track from the nearest road is the village of Deenabandu. The people of Deenabandu are, in one way at least, fortunate. Their village is the base for a voluntary health project. It is a relatively successful and pioneering one. Dr. Prem Chandran John, the project director, is sometimes asked to help OXFAM in evaluating its health work. His advice and experience are highly valued. "I always try to look at the greatest problems affecting the greatest number," says Dr. John. "This means agricultural labourers."[1]

Agricultural workers are the largest and the poorest group of working people — nearly three-quarters of the labour force of the poorest countries[2], the mass of the rural poor. The World Bank's Development Report for 1980 says:

> "Nor is there any serious disagreement about who the poor are... with the partial exception of Latin America (where about 40% are in the towns) the poor are primarily rural dwellers, overwhelmingly dependent on agriculture — the majority of them landless (or nearly landless) labourers."[3]

The usual concept of the Third World's poor concerns the things they have and, more often, the things they do not have — they are seen as frustrated consumers. But they are also producers. They often work long and hard in the heat and the dust. And yet, too often, their reward is hunger and ill-health.

Consumers in the rich world greatly depend on the produce of the Third World's agricultural workers. Without them the supermarket shelves would be bare of tea, coffee, cocoa and bananas. Cotton would be in short supply and there would be no rubber for the tyres of bicycles or cars. Of course, there are now artificial substitutes for some of these products, but the poor still provide many things which rich world consumers value in their daily lives.

It is easy to take the labour of the poor for granted, yet all the products mentioned, and many more, are produced at some risk to the workers. Attempts to increase the productivity of agriculture have also made it more hazardous.

The Director General of the International Labour Organisation (ILO) has said that,

> "Wherever agriculture has been modernised there has been a large increase in employment injuries both through the aggravation of traditional hazards and through appearance of new ones".[4]

New techniques and ideas are being introduced into Third World agriculture which have a profound effect on the socio-economic position of agricultural workers, on their health, and on the productivity of the land.

One central aspect of these changes common to virtually every country is the arrival and increasing use of chemical pesticides. The ravages of pests (insects, weeds, plant diseases etc.) need to be controlled. Pesticides bring a promise — a promise of higher yields, of more food for the hungry, and of freedom from the diseases spread by insects — in short, the promise of an easier and a better

3

life. But pesticides also bring a new hazard into the lives of agricultural workers. A recent World Health Organisation (WHO) Workshop expressed concern:

"Today, with the introduction of pesticides, chemicals and machinery into rural sectors, the problems which until now had been noted and dealt with in industrial settings are appearing in rural areas... Responsible agencies and health organisations must become aware of these new health hazards."[5]

Pesticides must be chosen and applied with care if ill-effects are to be avoided. Yet, under Third World conditions, such care may be difficult to ensure.

Back in Deenabandu some very hazardous pesticides were in the hands of the farmers. The instructions on their labels indicate some of the difficulties which Third World people face in pursuing the promise of pesticides. The labels say such things as: "Store in a cool dark and dry place", "use rubber gloves and face masks" and "in case of accident call a physician". In Deenabandu there is a doctor nearby, but in most rural areas of the Third World the nearest physician could be hours away. A cool place is hard to find, and rubber gloves and face masks virtually impossible. On one of the bottles, the instructions were not in the local language. And anyway 65% of the people cannot read.

It is not only the health of the worker which is threatened by these factors, but also the effectiveness of the pest management strategy. Indiscriminate and improper use of pesticides may be unprofitable, ineffective or even counterproductive, in the long term if not immediately. The pests' natural enemies are killed by the pesticides and the pests themselves develop the ability to resist the action of the chemicals. A kind of addiction can set in where the farmer must apply more, and more powerful, pesticides in order to prevent devastating crop losses. This process has been described as the 'pesticide treadmill' and its action can accentuate all the difficulties of pesticide use to the point of crisis.

Yet the need for pest control is a powerful one and pesticides are potentially an extremely important part of the answer to that need. In most Third World countries it is reckoned that at least a third of potential crops are lost to pests.[6] There are other factors which hold back agricultural production and keep the poor hungry. Low wages, the unequal distribution of land, and lack of access to water and credit, are among the most important. Improvements in these areas are essential, but there is no denying that the control of pest damage can play a significant part in improving the lives of the poor.

As well as damaging crops some pests, especially insects, also represent a direct threat to human health. Diseases carried by insects include yellow fever, river blindness, elephantiasis, sleeping sickness and malaria. About 1,000 million people, most of them in the Third World, are at risk from malaria alone.[7] It is a disease which weakens people and reduces their ability to work effectively. Because they are unable to produce enough for their basic needs, people suffer from malnutrition and so are more susceptible to disease. This is the vicious cycle of poverty and disease which needs to be broken. One way to break the cycle is to control the mosquitoes which carry malaria.

Pesticides have brought the promise of an effective weapon against the pests which devastate crops and the insects which spread disease. If they are properly used pesticides can indeed help to fulfil this promise. In Britain food production relies heavily on pesticides which have helped to increase yields by over 2% a year for the past two decades.[8] In the USA, Professor David Pimentel has cal-

4

culated that the removal of all pesticides from US agriculture would raise crop losses to pests from 33% to 42%. Even after taking account of some of the indirect social and environmental 'costs' of pesticide use, Pimentel estimates a net dollar return of three to one on money spent on pesticides in the USA.[9]

In the Third World, too, experiments have demonstrated the enormous potential of pesticides in securing increases in crop yields. For example, chemical weeding of groundnuts two and four weeks after sowing can increase yields by as much as 179%. Experiments at the International Rice Research Institute in the Philippines between 1964 and 1971 showed that rice plots protected by insecticides yielded an average of 2.7 tons per hectare more than unprotected plots – almost double the yield. Similarly, the use of rodenticides can result in rice yields two or three times higher than those of untreated plots.[10]

Although experimental results are not always matched in farmers' fields, the benefits of pesticide use are not merely theoretical. These benefits are especially important to countries which rely heavily on agricultural production. In Ghana, for example, cocoa exports contribute some 60% of foreign exchange earnings. The use of insecticides to control capsid bugs there has been shown to increase cocoa yields by up to 244% and to have saved at least 70,000 tons from destruction in the late 1960s.[11] It has also been estimated that without the use of insecticides some 50% of Third World cotton production would be destroyed by pests.[12]

In the field of public health, and especially of malaria control, the use of pesticides has saved many lives. The invention of DDT gave birth to the hope that malaria could be banished from the earth by shortening the lives of the mosquitoes which carry the disease. A global malaria eradication policy was adopted by the WHO in 1955 and it has been estimated that by 1970 the campaign had prevented 2,000 million cases of malaria and saved 15 million lives.[13] Despite later setbacks, pesticides continue to play an effective part in the control of malaria and of other vector-borne diseases in the Third World.[14]

Lim and Ong of the Malaysian Agricultural Research and Development Institute have summarised the potential benefits of pesticides:

> "To date, many pesticides are noted to be highly effective
> and economical to use. They are generally also more adaptable
> for a wide range of situations, including the rapid control of
> outbreak populations. Not only can these chemicals be
> marshalled quickly to ensure immediate impact but also their
> employment could be readily executed over a large area within
> a short time."[15]

This then is the promise. What of the pests and the pesticides themselves? It seems obvious that pesticides are substances which have the purpose and the ability to kill pests. But it is not quite so simple. Firstly, the term 'pests' does not include only insects. Also included are weeds, plant diseases, rodents and nematodes. Also, different people have different ideas about the usefulness (or troublesomeness) of a particular plant or insect. Such perceptions of pests, and of pesticides, are obviously a crucial factor in the system under consideration. This system does not only include pests and chemicals. It also includes farmers and farm workers who see things in their own way and are, in their turn, part of an economic and social system through which work, food, land, money and status are distributed.

It is the interests of people — growers and consumers — which are paramount. They are the priority, and the pest is considered only in terms of its ultimate effects upon them. Pesticides too need to be considered primarily in terms of their impact on people.

A pest is an organism having an undesirable effect on crops, livestock, or health — an animal or plant living where people would prefer it not to live, at least in such large numbers. A pesticide is a substance which kills the pest, or otherwise modifies the pest population. It is important to understand though, that pesticides do not kill only pests. Most are also capable of killing other plants or insects or, in sufficient dosage, human beings.

Pesticides can be categorised in two main ways — by the type of pest upon which they are designed to act, or by their chemical make-up. The former gives us insecticides (for insects), herbicides (for weeds), fungicides (for plant diseases) and so on. The latter gives, for example, organochlorines (which include DDT, endrin, dieldrin and BHC, also known as HCH); organophosphates (such as parathion, malathion, diazinon, dimethoate and many others ending in 'phos'); carbamates (carbofuran, aldicarb, carbaryl etc) and pyrethroids.

This book, while referring to many types of pesticide, will concentrate especially on insecticides. This is because Third World pesticide consumption is dominated by insecticides[16] and because problems with insects and insecticides most clearly illustrate the issues.

It will be seen that pesticides are called by many different names.[17] In this book the standard, generic names (beginning with small letters, eg paraquat) of the active ingredients will be used, except when discussing the products of particular companies, which have their own brand names (beginning with a capital letter, eg Gramoxone). The active ingredients used in pesticide formulations also have their particular chemical names. These will be avoided except where there is no standard name to use.

Pesticide use worldwide each year is roughly a pound weight for every man, woman and child on earth and the world pesticide market is growing in both volume and value. Between 1972 and 1980 the market grew in real terms by an annual average growth rate of 5%.[18] By volume, pesticide use is expected to grow from 1,900 million kgs (4,100 million pounds weight) in 1976 to 2,300 million kgs (5,000 million pounds) by 1985.[19]

The Third World uses about 15% of the pesticides,[20] including some 30% of the world's insecticides.[21] Average pesticide use in the Third World is nearly 100 grams (3.5 oz) per annum for every person. This is considerably less than in the rich countries but the value of Third World imports grew at an average rate of 15% a year between 1974 and 1977.[22]

UK Pesticide exports to the Third World have grown very rapidly in recent years — by 211% in value over the four years 1975-9. In 1979 they amounted to 66.008 tonnes, worth more than £92 million.[23] In 1978, the UK accounted for 12.2% of the world pesticide export market, an increase from 9.1% in 1974. This compares to a US share of 16.5% in 1978. UK exports are a part of the giant European Economic Community (EEC) share of 61.5%.[24] Western Europe as a whole exported some 4.5 times the value of pesticides as the US.[25] More details on UK pesticide exports are given in Appendix II.

The policy decisions of European governments and manufacturers have an impact on Third World people through the export, formulation and sale of pesticides. Britain and the other exporting countries have a responsibility to ensure that policies are formulated in the interests of the Third World's poor as well as in the interests of sales and profitability for the country of origin, its companies and their shareholders. These policies should surely be directed towards ensuring the maximum safety and efficacy of pesticide use in the Third World.

In order to adopt the best policies in both exporting and importing countries and internationally, it is necessary to understand the problems which can arise if such policies are not pursued. In order to do things right, it is necessary to know what can go wrong. Descriptions of the benefits of pesticide use mean little unless they are weighed against the problems, and unless it is known to whom the benefits accrue and upon whom the adverse consequences fall. The aim must be to fulfil the promise of pesticides for the poor whilst minimising the ill-effects which fall upon them.

This book will examine the problems which arise from the use of pesticides for the purposes for which they were designed -- the improvement of agricultural production and the control of disease. It does not argue that these are the greatest problems currently facing the poor. In terms of their direct impact on health through pesticide poisoning, they are relatively insignificant when compared to the major killers -- malnutrition, and the lack of clean drinking water and adequate sanitation. Nevertheless, pesticide poisoning is essentially preventable and the pesticide exporting countries have a potentially significant role to play in its prevention. In addition, the long-term impact of pesticide misuse in terms of resistance and the pesticide treadmill, together with the threat which resistance still holds for vector control programmes, is far-reaching indeed. If responsible action is not taken in time, the consequences of these problems will threaten the health and food supply of millions of the poor. These problems are worrying enough already, but they also have disaster potential.

The proper use of pesticides in the Third World means taking account of the social and economic realities of life. It means using pesticides which can be safely applied by relatively untrained, often illiterate workers, without the need for elaborate protective equipment. If the promise of pesticides is to be fulfilled, their use should be complementary to the best traditional farming practices and integrated with non-chemical methods of pest control. They should be applied only when necessary, and pest management should go hand in hand with *pesticide* management -- the involvement of the community with health and agricultural services to ensure that pesticides are used safely and efficiently.

This combination of measures essentially describes the concept of integrated pest management (IPM). IPM does not mean the complete abandonment of pesticides. In fact the use of pesticides as part of an IPM programme is the best use of pesticides. The problems and prospects of IPM in the Third World, and the role of pesticides in such programmes are the subject of Chapter 10 of this book. These issues are raised here in order to emphasise OXFAM's position on pesticides. OXFAM is in no way opposed to pesticides *per se*. Properly used in the appropriate social context, the right pesticides can help to improve the lives of poor people. Indeed, they have an essential role to play in agriculture and public health both in the present and for the foreseeable future. Any attempt

7

to discuss the important issues of pesticide use in the Third World in terms of 'pesticides' versus 'no pesticides' is merely to obscure the real issues.

The first two chapters of this book are devoted to the two major factors in the pesticide treadmill: the impact of pesticides on the complex ecology of the farmer's field and especially on those species which are the natural enemies of pests, and the manner and degree of pests' ability to circumvent the chemical onslaught — the development of resistance by pests to pesticides.

Their contribution to malaria control has been pesticides' greatest achievement. Millions of lives have been saved. But there have been problems and setbacks even here. Chapter 3 looks at the use of pesticides in the control of malaria, and especially at the way in which the insects which carry disease have also developed resistance, sometimes assisted by the uncontrolled use of pesticides in agriculture.

Chapter 4 takes a detailed look at the human cost of inappropriate and ill-advised pesticide use — the death and injury of many thousands of Third World people. Chapters 5 and 6 deal with the residues of pesticides in food and in the environment. Chapters 7 and 8 try to balance the costs and benefits of agricultural pesticide use in the Third World and examine how those costs and benefits are distributed. These chapters seek to answer the question of how far pesticides actually help in feeding the hungry.

Chapter 9 focuses specifically on the question of how pesticides are promoted, advertised and labelled in the Third World.

Chapter 10 describes the concept of integrated pest management in greater detail and discusses its implementation in the Third World. This chapter is an attempt to learn from the problems in order to find a better road for the future — a road where pesticides can take their place as a useful tool in Third World agriculture.

Chapter 11 discusses policies and makes recommendations which can bring that future closer, and help to avoid the suffering and distress which can result from inappropriate and uncontrolled sale and use of pesticides in the Third World.

The final section of each chapter describes some changes which could be made to improve things for the poor. Conveniently, although the subject matter of each chapter is different, many of the suggestions point in the same direction. A summary of recommendations is given at the end of Chapter 11.

Action in support of the poor is something in which everyone can play a part, however small. When you have read this book perhaps you will be ready to add your voice, with OXFAM, to the voice, too often unspoken, unheard or un-heeded, of the poor.

John Loftus/ARSAP

This Sri Lankan operator is wearing protective clothing. In hot or humid conditions in the Third World few are keen to dress this way. Ignorance of the dangers, uncaring or ill-informed employers and unenforced or non-existent regulations mean that few do.

Pesticides and Natural Enemies

PESTICIDES AND NATURAL ENEMIES

Anisar Aguilar grows tomatoes in the village of Comarapa in the humid subtropics of Bolivia. He and his friends have always had problems with pests, but in 1968 a new one appeared. Three years after they began to use pesticides, these farmers were faced with a devastating infestation of a new kind of moth.[1] In many parts of the Third World similar things have been happening.[2] Some farmers have found that after using pesticides their existing pest problems have got worse or else that old pests have been replaced by new ones. These problems are the result of the combination of two factors: the wide (broad spectrum) killing properties of many pesticides, and the especially great ecological diversity and complexity of insect life in the fields of the Third World.

There are at least a million species of insect on earth. Of this teeming mass of life, only a few thousand have become pests.[3] Of the remainder many are innocuous and most are probably beneficial. Some of these beneficial insects help, like bees, by pollinating the plants or providing us with food. Many insects and other creatures help by preying on troublesome species. Perhaps the best known of these predators are the spider and the ladybird which reduce the populations of flies and of aphids.

Apart from the 5,000 to 15,000 pest species, there are perhaps ten times as many which have pest potential. That is, they compete with human beings for plant material, yet their effects are hardly noticed. This is because their numbers are kept in check by climate, by lack of food or by their natural enemies — the predators and parasites which feed upon them.

The complex interplay of pest and predator, of crops, farm animals and man, is called an 'agro-ecosystem'. The addition of pesticides to a tropical agro-ecosystem, while it may help to reduce the pest population, can also give rise to two main kinds of difficulty. First, it may kill many of the natural enemies of the target pest, or else the population of natural enemies may take longer to recover from the pesticide application than do the pests. Thus freed from some of the natural controls which previously acted upon it, the population of the original pest may explode to unprecedented numbers.

The second kind of problem occurs when the pesticide kills large numbers of the natural enemies of a species other than the target pest, but having pest potential. This insect, perhaps previously unnoticed, may then be able to reproduce relatively unhindered to the detriment of the farmer and his crops. The arrival of a new pest in this way is known as a 'secondary' pest outbreak.

The ability of a pesticide to produce exactly the opposite of its intended effect has been well demonstrated in field experiments. University of California entomologist (insect specialist), Professor Paul DeBach, for example, has shown that by carefully timed and measured applications of pesticides it is quite possible to *increase* the pest population by as much as 1,250 times.[4]

If the desired effects are to be achieved, pesticides need to be correctly applied. This means first, that the particular pest responsible for damage must be correctly identified. Next, the farmer has to decide whether the damage caused is sufficient to warrant the expenditure in time and money necessary to counteract it and if it is, whether a chemical spray is the best method. Then the right pesticide has to be applied in the correct quantity at the most appropriate time. Even large farmers and plantations can go wrong — it is much more difficult for the small farmer.

One such small farmer is Hem Bahadur and his story illustrates the problems. He works as a night watchman in the Kathmandu valley of Nepal and supplements his wage by cultivating a small plot (0.4 hectares) of rice. His rice harvest helps to feed his wife and six small children. One day Hem Bahadur found that his rice plants were dying, and at the base of the plants were some small red 'caterpillars' or worms, which he assumed to be responsible. The night watchman was only prevented from spraying his field with a potentially dangerous insecticide by the assistance of his American employer. She and Hem Bahadur took some of the ailing rice plants, complete with worms, to the government agricultural research station, only to find that these particular creatures were 'a positive agent' in the rice field. The real problem, it emerged, was caused by a fungus. Had Hem Bahadur sprayed his field with the insecticide offered him by the local shopkeeper his problems could have become worse rather than better.[5]

Even the pests themselves are necessary to the maintenance of the agro-ecosystem. Control by natural enemies is an extremely energy-efficient system — it runs on the energy of the pest itself. The pest is the food supply of its own enemies. Cut off this food supply and the natural enemies may be depleted too much to deal with a later outbreak.

Natural enemies are so effective, says entomologist, Professor Ray F. Smith, that "they are commonly quite sufficient, in the absence of disturbing practices, for the adequate control of some of our most serious pest species".[6] In fact, according to an Organisation for Economic Co-operation and Development (OECD) Steering Group which looked at pest control problems of small farmers in the Third World:

"In small farmer food crops not exposed to repeated heavy applications of synthetic organic pesticides, indigenous natural enemies play an important role in keeping populations of potentially destructive species at levels that allow the farmer to harvest a crop adequate to the simple needs of his family."[7]

This role of natural enemies is especially important to the poorest farmers who can ill afford the purchase of pesticides, but for whom a severe pest outbreak may mean no food for the family.

The loss of natural biological controls could be the first step on to the pesticide treadmill. The farmer's first response to a pest resurgence or a secondary pest outbreak is often to spray more. This may lead to more problems, and more sprays, until the farmer must run forever faster in order to stay in the same place. The potential of pest species to develop resistance to pesticides accelerates the process, which can eventually put farmers out of business or even bring the whole nations to the brink of bankruptcy.[8] For the small farmer, or the labourer on a larger farm, the risks to health from contact with toxic sprays also increase as the treadmill spins faster.

The history of cotton production in Central America[9] is a classic illustration of the treadmill in action. In the first quarter of the twentieth century, Central American farmers began to grow cotton, keeping pests down by natural control, picking off insects by hand, and by the use of a low level of pesticides such as infusions of tobacco leaves. They were troubled by three pests, the red boll weevil, the leafworm and the desert locust. Of these, some producers said, only the first was a major problem. After 1945, a successful campaign was launched against the desert locust and in the 1950s intensive use of machinery and chemicals began. The new synthetic pesticides led to increased yields. At first insecticides were applied about eight times a season.

By the mid-'50s, three new pest species including the bollworm had appeared, apparently due to increasing pesticide use. During the 1960s Central America became a boom market for pesticide manufacturers, often experimenting with chemicals not approved for sale in their own countries. As many as 50 alternatives were on offer for a single pest. The number of applications reached 28 a season. Two pest species ceased to be so important, but were replaced by four new ones, including the army worm and the whitefly. The combination of new pests and resistance to pesticides led to the application of ever greater quantities until pest control accounted for 50% of cotton production costs. Even so yields began to decline. By the early '70s there were eight important pest species and spray applications reached 40 a season in some areas.

The massive Gezira scheme in the Sudan[10] grows cotton which brings in nearly half the country's foreign exchange. But production costs have quadrupled in the last ten years while yields have fallen by 40%. The pesticide treadmill has played an important part in this disaster on the world's largest farm. Other factors include difficulties in maintaining irrigation channels, and management problems. A large irrigated scheme such as this can operate successfully only if the distribution of inputs is efficient and farm operations properly co-ordinated.

The two million acres of the Gezira are farmed by tenants who grow ten acres of cotton each as well as a few food crops. In the Gezira the use of pesticides has led to resistance and the destruction of natural enemies. The number of applications has increased by seven to nine times since chemical pesticides were introduced in the 1940s, and some pest species have arrived on the scene in unprecedented numbers. One of these, the whitefly, excretes a sticky substance which makes it impossible to process the cotton in modern mills. According to a United Nations (UN) panel of experts, cotton production in the Sudan is close to disaster. With the help of the experts, a rescue operation has begun, but the Gezira remains a classic example of the potential ill-effects of the pesticide treadmill.

Cotton is notoriously susceptible to pests and accounts for more than a quarter of worldwide insecticide use. But it is not just on cotton that the treadmill takes its costly toll. Rice, the staple food of hundreds of millions of Asian people, has been severely affected in the last ten years or so.

All over South and South-east Asia, an insect called the brown planthopper is consuming the people's food at an unprecedented rate — it is now probably Asia's most damaging rice pest. And yet ten years ago it was a pest of only minor importance. The planting of two or three rice crops a year has given the planthopper a year-round food supply and the new wonder rice varieties of the green revolution have replaced traditional ones which were apparently more resistent to planthopper attack.

These changes in agricultural methods have increased pest problems, necessitating pesticide applications which have been the first step on the treadmill and laid the foundations for epidemics of brown planthopper. Dr J.P. Kulshrestha is an entomologist in the Indian state of Orissa. He is running a programme aimed at rescuing this situation by reducing reliance on pesticides.

"The time-bound insecticidal schedules which were advocated with high-yielding varieties led to the resurgence of several insect pests which were of minor importance earlier. The widespread epidemics of brown planthopper in Kerala in 1973, in Andhra Pradesh in 1975-76, in Tamil Nadu, Orissa and West Bengal in 1976 are examples of this kind. Further studies revealed that indiscriminate use of insecticides upset the natural equilibrium between pests and their natural enemies thereby allowing pests to multiply without natural checks. The experience has shown that use of pesticide alone can not solve the pest problem in rice."[11]

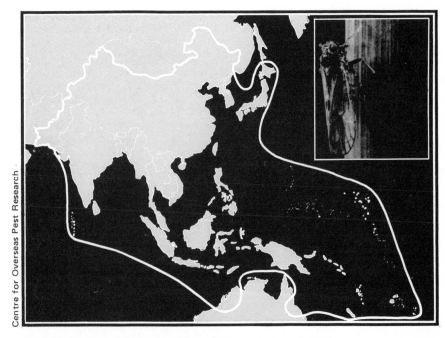

Centre for Overseas Pest Research

Fig. 1 Distribution of Brown Planthopper *(Nilaparvata Ingens)*, 1982. Inset, Brown Planthopper.

In the Tanjong Karang area of Malaysia in 1977, a hopper attack took three months to control at a cost of about £45,000. Yet the following year the hopper was back, causing nearly £450,000 worth of damage in the same area. In 1979, the hoppers extended their range to the Kedah district, threatening thousands of acres of rice. The insect sucks the juices of the plant creating vast brown areas known as 'hopperburn'.[12]

The appearance of brown planthoppers, once an insignificant pest and now liberated from their natural enemies, causes rice farmers to panic. Their livelihood is at stake. The resulting heavy applications of often highly toxic pesticides may not only accentuate their future problems, but also expose them to a serious health hazard. The planthopper epidemic creates in its turn an epidemic of pesticide poisoning. In the Kegalle district of Sri Lanka in the summer of 1978 about 500 acres were affected of which 300 were totally destroyed by the planthopper. There were over a thousand cases of pesticide poisioning in that district alone, mostly from the three worst hit areas.[13]

In Sri Lanka, the hopper problem has only occurred to a serious extent in the last five years or so.[14] Mr Jayakoddy, Assistant Director of Agriculture for Gampaha district, explained that the hopper problem gets worse every year. Poorer farmers, he said, find it difficult because they have to pay out more money for pesticides before the harvest brings in their income.[15]

Entomologist Guy Rajendram is funded by OXFAM to carry out research on the brown planthopper in Sri Lanka, with the objective of finding biological alternatives to reliance on pesticides. Such biological control would depend on the identification and use of natural predators and parasites of the planthopper. One potentital predator has been found, but the urgency of this kind of work, and indeed of dealing with the excessive or indiscriminate use of pesticides, remains evident. Rajendram reports that, in the 1979/80 'maha' season (September to March), nearly 30,000 acres of paddy were seriously damaged by the pest" due in large measure to excessive reliance on insecticides".[16]

Another OXFAM-funded development organisation in Sri Lanka is the Sarvodaya Movement. Sarvodaya works very closely with Sri Lanka's small rice farmers and encourages considerable caution in the use of pesticides. Sarvodaya leader A.T. Arayaratne says:

"In trying to increase yields in agriculture in Sri Lanka people have also increased the dependence on chemicals and this has resulted in the introduction of pests and weeds which were never previously a problem."[17]

Sarvodaya has a number of farms of its own as well as employing agricultural officers and advisors, but "the propagation of these methods of agriculture is very weak" says Mr Arayaratne, "compared to the advertisements of the chemical companies". This emphasises the necessity, if the poor are to be free of the ill-effects of the pesticide treadmill, of ensuring that all channels of communication with the farmer are fully used to encourage sensible, safe and cautious use of pesticides.

* * * * * *

In order to keep off the treadmill, pesticide use should be kept to the minimum consistent with acceptable levels of pest control. This means making maximum use of non-chemical alternatives and developing, selecting and using chemicals

14

in such a way as to protect and preserve the natural enemies of pest species. Pesticides, for all their value, do not provide a universal panacea. It is important that all available information channels to the farmer should stress caution and point out that excessive or inappropriate use of pesticides can lead to pest resurgence and secondary outbreaks. These channels include training programmes, agricultural extension services, labels, advertisements and sales representatives. Farmers should be encouraged to make use of a variety of cultural, mechanical and biological pest management techniques in conjunction with suitable pesticide application.

Effective utilization of biological management requires stricter control and better information on pesticide use. Indiscriminate pesticide use can seriously damage pest management programmes which depend on the survival of indigenous or specially introduced predators and parasites.

A study conducted by Cornell University as long ago as 1971, emphasised the importance of natural enemies in pest management in South-east Asia.

"The potential for pest population explosions in the tropics is so
great that every effort is needed to utilize selective control agents
and practices that will not destroy the natural control systems."[18]

Their warning, it seems, has not been sufficiently heeded and the results are only too apparent. Five years later, Professor Smith put the point more strongly.

"Extended control of the complex of pest species is unlikely to be
achieved unless natural enemies are made a prime consideration."[19]

This exhortation needs not merely to be repeated, but to be acted upon by all agencies concerned with pest control and with the welfare of the poor in the Third World — the pesticide industry as well as governmental and international organisations.

The Problem of Resistance

THE PROBLEM OF RESISTANCE

In the Rio Grande Valley of Mexico, cotton production has virtually disappeared; 700,000 acres were abandoned in 1970. Cotton gins, compresses and oil mills went out of business; farmworkers moved away in search of work elsewhere. A once prosperous community was plunged into social and economic depression. This disaster occurred when the tobacco budworm, an important cotton pest, became resistant to a wide range of pesticides. University of California entomologist Professor Ray F. Smith said in 1974: "Their resistant strains cannot be controlled by any available insecticide at any dosage."

The tobacco budworm was once kept under control by natural enemies. It became a serious pest when these were wiped out by pesticides used against the boll weevil and other pests threatening the cotton crop. As it developed resistance, more and more pesticides were used. Farmworkers often became ill from the pesticides, but the budworm went from strength to strength. In northeastern Mexico alone it wiped out, almost totally, cotton crops worth £35 million a year.[1]

The problems of resistance and those of toxicity to non-target organisms commonly interact to speed the spin of the pesticide treadmill. As it whirls faster, crop production becomes more costly and less economic, environmental and residue problems build up, workers and domestic animals are poisoned, exports are turned away and diseases spread by insects reach epidemic proportions. The scale of such disasters has already been significant and worse could be on the way.

Insects, with their rapid breeding cycles and genetic diversity, are well placed to evolve the ability to shrug off our attempts at chemical control. The point has been strongly argued by University of California entomologist, the late Professor Robert van den Bosch:

"In ignoring the ecological nature of pest control and in attempting to dominate insects with a simplistic chemical control strategy, we played directly into the strength of those formidable adversaries. As a result, today, only a third of a century after the discovery of DDT's insect-killing powers and despite the subsequent development of scores of potent poisons, the bugs are doing better than ever, and much of insect control is a shambles."[2]

And it is not just insects. Rodents, fungi, bacteria and even weeds have also begun to resist some pesticides. In 1976, there were 67 different pathogens (fungi and bacteria) resistant to at least one chemical, a figure which had almost doubled in two years from 35 in 1974. Even this may be an underestimate.[3]

By 1976, 19 weed species had developed resistance to a total of 17 herbicides. This may, as with fungicide resistance, represent a considerable underestimate.[4] In addition, there are now at least seven species of rat resistant to rodenticides, including the common black rat which is now widely resistant to warfarin.[5] Nevertheless, it is with the insects (and mites and ticks) that the major problems occur. By 1980 there were 432 species of arthropods in which resistance had been documented to at least one pesticide. These included 171 of medical or veterinary significance and a further 261 important for agriculture. These figures represent a stage in an accelerating process: the number of resistant species more than trebled between 1960 (137 species) and 1980.[6]

The problems discussed in the last chapter are the result of the propensity of pesticides to kill and injure organisms other than the target species. The resistance problem is of a different type. It concerns the ability of evolution to adapt species to life in a new kind of world -- a world in which pesticides are increasingly commonplace. The potentially disastrous interaction of these two types of problem is accentuated by the unfortunate fact that the pests seem able to develop resistance to pesticides which are still killing their enemies.

Of the 225 resistant species documented up to 1971, only 4 were natural enemies of pests[7], and by 1976 there were only 8.[8] This is thought to be due to differences in the potential for increase after spraying. Surviving pests have a more or less unlimited food supply, with less competition for the plant material. Their predators, on the other hand, suffer both from the pesticide and from a dramatic reduction in their food supply -- the pest. Other natural enemies belong to types having a general inability to develop resistance.[9]

The speed with which a pest will develop resistance depends on a number of factors, not all of them fully understood. Essentially though, an insect's propensity for resistance depends on its genetic make-up together with the length and nature of its life cycle, including its behaviour, its reproductive power and feeding habits. These insect characteristics are largely beyond our control, but the other side of the equation is not. This includes the type of pesticide chosen, the rate and timing of its application and its place in a wider pest management strategy.

The use of a pesticide favours the survival of that portion of the pest population with genetic or behavioural characteristics which allow it to reduce the amount of chemical entering its body, to de-toxify the chemical in its body or to otherwise survive the effects of the poison. As these insects reproduce, their ability to survive is passed on to their offspring until a greater and greater proportion of the pest population are of the resistant type.

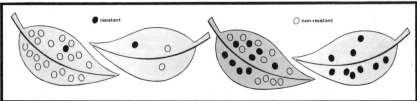

Fig. 2 Spraying increases the proportion of resistant insects, making subsequent applications of pesticide less effective.

There are a few fortunate anomalies where pesticides have remained effective over long periods, but these have been described by one author as "collectors' items" and in general "one must now expect any insecticide to induce resistance to itself in any target pest".[10] In the tropical and subtropical areas of the Third World such resistance can develop very rapidly.[11]

Cotton has so far been the crop to suffer most from resistance problems, but all field crops are affected to some degree. Rice in particular, the staple food crop for millions of the poor, is under threat, especially in South-east Asia. Other staples like alfalfa, maize and sorghum so far have fewer resistant pests, but those species which have developed resistance are the 'key' ones which threaten crops year after year.[12]

The problems are aggravated further by some of the characteristics of resistance development. Sometimes, for example, a genetic or behavioural trait which enables a pest to withstand one pesticide may also confer resistance to another. This 'cross-resistance' occurs especially between chemicals of the same class (eg organophosphates) and can mean that substituting a new chemical fails to hold off the problem. A number of resistance mechanisms can confer resistance to a number of pesticides and as one pesticide is substituted for another, the pest may develop 'multiple resistance' to a whole sequence of chemicals.

As the sequence proceeds, the number of new options is rapidly reduced until, in extreme cases, we are faced with pest populations highly resistant to virtually all available pesticides.[13]

The diamond-back moth, a pest of cabbages in the Cameron Highlands of the Malay peninsular, is a case in point.[14] The resistance problem has developed to the point where many farmers are having to spray three times a week, 65% of them with 'cocktails' made up of two or more different pesticides mixed together. In a 1977 survey eleven different insecticides were being used, often until less than a week before harvest and in dosages considerably higher than those recommended on the labels.

Since the 1950s a succession of pesticides has been used against the diamond-back moth with new ones every year or two. Some degree of resistance now exists to at least eleven insecticides and is suspected for others. These include members of all the major groups, including even the new pyrethroids. Writing in 1980, Professor Gordon Conway of London's Imperial College summed up the prospects:

> "Once resistance has become widespread to the synthetic
> pyrethroids and to the growth regulators currently under trial
> against the diamond-back moth, there will be no further chemical
> insecticides available. This point could well be reached in three to
> five years."[15]

Even in 1978, Malaysian researchers, Ooi and Sudderuddin, were describing the sitution as "desperate" and insecticides were accounting for nearly a third of the production cost of the cabbages. Growing cabbages in the Cameron Highlands is rapidly becoming uneconomic.

It might be assumed that after some lapse of time a pesticide abandoned due to resistance could be re-introduced and be useful again. This, however, does not seem to be the case; the resistance is rapidly regained. House-flies in Denmark for example recovered in two months the DDT resistance that had taken them five years to lose and two years to develop in the first place. In the words of one entomologist, "our accomplishment has a certain permanence".[16]

Summing up the findings of Food and Agriculture Organisation (FAO) surveys another writer demonstrates the scale of this understatement:

"No instances have been reported where field resistance has declined sufficiently to enable re-introduction of a formerly effective pesticide to which resistance had developed."[17]

Because of this, says Dr. Sawicki of the Rothamsted Experimental Station,

"established resistance can be dealt with only by switching to alternative pesticides to which there is no resistance. This, however, is a transient solution because with time resistance develops to the alternative, which must be replaced by yet another compound. Each new insecticide selects in turn one or more mechanisms of resistance, and each mechanism usually confers resistance to several insecticides."[18]

Thus, our ability to control important insect pests is seriously threatened, especially in the tropical and sub-tropical regions of the Third World. The resistance problem makes the continued reliance on chemical pesticides as our sole means of pest control impossible. Experts from London's Imperial College have made this point forcefully:

"Induced resistance cannot be over-emphasised as the key factor jeopardising the continued and successful use of vitally important chemicals."[19]

"The development of resistance, more than anything else, demonstrates the dangers of over-dependence on a single method of control".[20]

The initial response to resistance usually consists in increasing the dose, with all the attendant environmental effects that this brings, including the increased threat to the health of farm labourers. In addition, the farmers' costs increase, especially when new pesticides are introduced in place of the old. The new ones are almost always more expensive. David Pimentel has estimated that in the USA, the extra insecticide costs due to resistance in agricultural pests amount to £51 million a year.[21]

Sudan

Let us look now at three examples of the treadmill in action. First to the Gezira, the fertile alluvial plain at the confluence of the White and Blue Niles in the Sudan. Since the 1940s the quantities of pesticides used, the area and proportion of the crop sprayed and the number of sprays per season, have steadily increased. By 1976, 2,500 tonnes of insecticides a year were being used in the Gezira. The increased cost of inseciticides imported into the Sudan between 1966/67 and 1980/81 will be over 1,400%.[22] The whitefly, released from its enemies by previous spraying, has tightened its grip on the hard-pressed Gezira and its 1.5 million residents and 400,000 seasonal labourers.

While cotton production costs have quadrupled in 10 years, yields have fallen from 420 kgs per hectare in the early '70s to 250 kgs/ha by 1980[23] — about the same as the yields obtained before World War Two and the widespread introduction of pesticides.[24] Increasing costs and falling yields have finally

Table 1

Area of Cotton Sprayed, Percentage of Cotton Area Sprayed, and Number of Applications/Year. 1946-1979.

Year	Cotton Sprayed Hectares	Cotton Sprayed Percentage of Area	Average Number Sprays/Year
1946	600	0.7	1.0
1947	3,500	4.0	1.0
1948	14,500	17.0	1.0
1949	32,700	37.0	1.0
1950	53,000	60.0	1.0
1951	70,000	80.0	1.0
1954	98,000	100.0	1.0
1959	158,000	100.0	1.0
1964	213,000	100.0	2.5
1969	246,000	100.0	4.9
1974	247,000	100.0	6.0
1976/7			6.5
1977/8			8.1
1978/9			9.3

Sources: Bartsch, *Economic Problems of Pest Control, examined for the case of the Gezira, Sudan,* London, 1978 (up to '74). FAO/UNEP "Report of 9th session of FAO/UNEP Panel of Experts on Integrated Pest Control", Sudan, 1979.

led to a reduction, in recent years, in the area under cotton in the Gezira. Table 1 illustrates the treadmill in action:

The problems of Sudanese cotton production are not due solely to the pest control crisis, but the significance of this factor was stressed by the Sudanese Minister of Agriculture in 1979. Opening a meeting of the FAO/United Nations Environment Programme (UNEP) Panel of Experts on Integrated Pest Control, he stressed that

"Whilst it is true that the underlying cause of reduction in yield and quality of cotton is a complex of interacting factors, it seems fairly sure that insect pests, mainly the cotton whitefly, are a major constraint."[25]

FAO/UNEP experts expect that the whitefly will shortly be "beyond effective chemical control". They have worked with local people to devise a short-term rescue operation based on delaying and reducing pesticide applications, ceasing to use those to which resistance has developed, and amending planting and harvesting times. They say, however, that

"this would not provide a long-lasting answer. This would only come from long-term research on resistant varieties, biological control, cultural practices, host manipulation and the judicious use of chemicals."[26]

Nicaragua

Disaster struck in the cotton fields of Nicaragua in the late 1960s.[27] Contributing over 20% of foreign exchange earnings, cotton is central to the Nicaraguan economy. With the introduction of pesticides in the 1950s, cotton in Central America boomed with yields reaching a peak in 1965.

> "But in the next five years the situation reached a crisis. Production decreased at an annual rate of 15.9% and the country came very close to bankruptcy. The primary cause of this situation was the failure to achieve control of the pests by the prevalent unilateral reliance on chemical pesticides. Problems of serious and increasing resistance to insecticides were evident."[28]

As the bollworm, the whitefly and other pests developed resistance, so the farmers applied higher dosages of pesticide at more and more frequent intervals. In some cases the number of applications reached 50 a season. The treadmill spun faster as new species came to the fore, freed, as discussed in Chapter 1, from the grip of their natural enemies. During the 1966/7 season an average hectare of cotton land in Nicaragua was 'blanketed' with 99.2 litres of liquid and 18.7 kgs or dust insecticides.

Pesticide marketing was not subject to controls and the farmer was choosing between as many as 75 different varieties, some of them not approved for use in their countries of origin.

> "That was the golden era for the pesticide companies which provided well remunerated technical agents to explain the pesticide failures, recommend new formulas and combinations and sell more and more products."[29]

As the pesticide applications increased, so the risk to human life also became greater. In 1969/70, there were over 3,000 poisoning cases including 383 deaths in Nicaragua.[30] At the same time malaria cases increased from 7,100 in 1968 to 28,500 in 1970.[31]

In the midst of this human and economic tragedy solutions began to be sought. With assistance from FAO and the University of California, an integrated pest management strategy was devised and began to be implemented in 1970. The use of the most toxic compounds, and those to which resistance was greatest, was reduced or discontinued and spray regimes implemented which would give maximum protection to natural enemies, based on continuous monitoring of the populations of pests and parasites.

> "It has been proved that the dosage and frequency of insecticide applications can be substantially reduced with no significant effects on yield. The cotton statistics themselves have shown that after a certain number of treatments the yield decreases as much as the number of applications increases."[32]

The new programme was successful in reducing insecticide use, increasing the profitability of the crop and reducing the incidence of poisoning. The achievements of the integrated pest management (IPM) programme in Nicaragua and its difficulties will be discussed further in Chapter 10.

East and South-east Asia

In other parts of the world, it seems, the same tragically familiar cycle is repeating itself. In India, for example, entomologist Dr. Veeresh of the Agricultural University in Bangalore makes the prediction that "within ten years, it will not be surprising if we're in the same position as Latin America".[33]

But what of the future for *food* production? Whilst "there are only limited grounds for concluding there is a threat to global food production", Professor Conway concludes that

"The greatest likelihood is of farm level resistance crises which accumulate to a national or regional loss of food production comparable to what has happened in cotton."[34]

The most likely such crises in the foreseeable future are in Third World countries. "The circumstances currently most favouring a crisis in a staple crop", says Conway, "occur in rice in East or South-east Asia."[35]

In 1965 eight rice pests were resistant to at least one insecticide and by 1975 there were fourteen.[36] We have seen, in Chapter 1, how pesticide use in rice has contributed to changes in the pest complex, with the brown planthopper causing, in some areas, total crop loss. Now resistance is an increasing problem. The treadmill is beginning to turn. In southern Japan, it has already begun with pesticide applications increasing from one or two a year in 1965 to as many as seven just five years later. The crisis there is held off by the temperate climate which restricts rice growing to a single season. Also Japan has no indigenous brown planthopper population. Professor Conway draws this ominous conclusion:

"The potential hazard is greater in tropical and sub-tropical South East Asia. There the introduction of the new high yielding varieties (HYVs) has brought about dramatic changes in rice cultivation, the structure of the rice agro-ecosystem and in particular the composition of the pest, disease and weed complexes... Severe brown planthopper outbreaks, in particular, have occurred... An outbreak covering 1.5 million hectares of HYVs occurred in South Korea in 1975 and in the same year losses in Indonesia to the brown planthopper and the virus [it carries] are reported to amount to about 290,000 tons. Resistance in the brown planthopper has been recorded in the Philippines and there is evidence that a number of insecticides actually stimulate reproduction in this pest...

Pesticide applications on rice in South East Asia have been low in the past but increasing severity of pest populations is producing a pressure for more intensive applications. Spraying or dusting of the rice plants is often needed at 10-14 day intervals... and since the new early maturing HYVs can now be grown continuously throughout the year on irrigated land, application rates of 10 to 20 times a year may become common. Under these conditions a severe resistance crisis could rapidly arise, possibly to both pests and pathogens."[37]

Substitution Strategy

The normal response to resistance is to spray more. When even this fails the next move is to substitute a new pesticide for the old one. These measures may slow the treadmill for a while but they do not solve the problem. Also, by using more, and perhaps more toxic, pesticides they can actually aggravate the side effects of the treadmill — the human cost in poisonings, environmental damage and increased incidence of malaria. The substitution strategy gives rise to another question of great significance to the future of pest control — will there always be another chemical to substitute? The answer may be no.

The continuous rush to invent new chemicals faster than the insects can develop resistance, even if it were possible, would be a very expensive and difficult solution. Already the insects are winning the race. While the number of resistant species increases faster and faster, the speed with which these species develop resistance to each new chemical also increases as they evolve a greater variety of resistance mechanisms or as existing mechanisms confer resistance to new chemicals, sometimes even before they have been introduced.[38] Meanwhile, the rate of introduction of new products is slowing down — from 25 a year in the late 1960s to 16 a year by 1979.[39] While the resistant species curve continues to increase, the new products curve is levelling off. This is especially clear in the case of insecticides (see Fig. 3).

The number of compounds which have to be checked to find one which will reach the commercial market was only 1,800 in 1956 and increased to 7,400 by 1970 and 12,000 by 1977.[40] This partly reflects the increased regulatory control over pesticides in the West. A new pesticide now has to go through stringent testing procedures, especially in the USA, before it can be registered. These tests and registration costs may constitute a third of the research and development (R&D) costs of a new product.[41] But, judging by the problems which have been caused by earlier pesticides, often leading to their withdrawal, it is surely wise to carry out such testing before the product reaches the market, regardless of regulatory requirements. Some standardisation of regulatory procedures between countries may help but if new pesticides are to be safe pesticides, these increased costs must be borne. This adds further to the need to make the safest and most sparing use possible of the pesticides available, and to give greater priority to alternative methods.

> "Potentially more serious in the long run," says Conway, "is the possibility that the decline in production of new compounds is also due to an exhaustion of a finite global number of chemical compounds with suitable pesticidal activity... we may be facing a resource depletion effect akin, say, to the utilisation of mineral resources or fossil fuels."[42]

The percentage of compounds passing the initial screening process declined from 3% in 1956 to 1% in 1970.[43] While the pesticide resource is probably still large, there is cause for concern here, and a further reason for conservation through more careful and limited pesticide use.

If looked at from a purely commercial point of view, the accelerating nature of resistance must present the pesticide industry with a dilemma. As long as resistance develops only slowly it provides the industry with the opportunity to market new products which yield relatively high profits due to patent protection. It is obviously not in the industry's interests, however, if resistance develops so quickly as to end a product's useful life before its R&D costs have been recouped. This latter scenario is becoming more likely as cross and multiple resistance reduce the lifetime of each new compound.

> "A factor facing research entomologists and industry personnel alike is the question of whether to use a pesticide aggressively and extensively for a shortened lifetime or conservatively for a longer period. Competitive products and the need to regain investment and show a profit as quickly as possible normally dictate the former."[44]

This strategy, though, is no longer acceptable, as the introduction of new

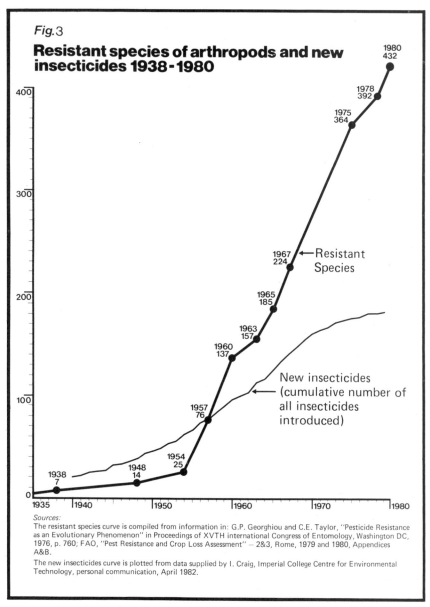

Fig.3

Resistant species of arthropods and new insecticides 1938-1980

1980
432

1978
392

1975
364

1967
224 ←Resistant Species

1965
185

1963
157

1960
137

New insecticides
(cumulative number of
all insecticides
introduced)

1957
76

1954
25

1948
14

1938
7

Sources:
The resistant species curve is compiled from information in: G.P. Georghiou and C.E. Taylor, "Pesticide Resistance as an Evolutionary Phenomenon" in Proceedings of XVTH international Congress of Entomology, Washington DC, 1976, p. 760; FAO, "Pest Resistance and Crop Loss Assessment" — 2&3, Rome, 1979 and 1980, Appendices A&B.

The new insecticides curve is plotted from data supplied by I. Craig, Imperial College Centre for Environmental Technology, personal communication, April 1982.

products cannot be relied upon to keep pace. We may also have reached the point where such a strategy ceases even to be in the economic interest of the industry itself. The industry's traditional stress on fast sales in the field may be working contrary to its long-term corporate interest, taking account of R&D criteria. The long-term effect of these dramatic changes on the pesticide industry is unclear, but in the USA there has already been a growth of small consultancy businesses offering a pest management package instead of just a bottle of chemical.

In the Third World, though, pesticides continue to be promoted as panaceas for farmers' problems.[45] In fact, the changing emphasis in pest management in the rich world could act to increase the pressure for sales in the Third World. Dr. Joyce Tait of Britain's Open University explains:

> "From research on pesticide usage by farmers in Europe and North America, it is apparent that there is little scope here for future growth in pesticide sales by the agrochemical industry, and as biological and integrated pest control systems are developed... pesticide usage may even decrease slightly." Yet, at the same time, says Tait, "The annual growth rate in pesticide sales... must be maintained in the future to finance the very high research and development costs involved in the production of new pesticides... Developing countries constitute the only market available to absorb this growth in pesticide sales."[46]

The need to minimise resistance problems demands less pesticide-dependent strategies. It is ironic that the adoption of these strategies in the rich world, combined with the need for new products, could be creating a sales pressure in the poor world, which could, in its turn, make it more difficult for the Third World to hold off resistance-induced crises.

The end result of these pressures could be a shift in pesticide-related problems from the rich world to the poor. Yet it is in the Third World where illiteracy, poor working conditions and malnutrition make the hazards most severe and where the tropical climate and new agricultural technology add to the pressures which lead to the pesticide treadmill.

* * * * * *

In the battle against resistance, the strategy of continually substituting new pesticides must be a last resort. Other measures should be taken to delay its necessity for as long as possible — not by using larger and larger doses of the existing compound, but by adopting a sensible strategy to avoid the development of resistance. This does not necessarily mean using lower dosages — if too low these can also add to resistance pressure. It means using pesticides in the correct dosages and less often — only when necessitated by a damaging pest population. In the longer-term it means reducing reliance on chemicals for managing pests, by incorporating pesticides into a wider strategy.

Firstly, all possible steps should be taken to inform farmers, especially small Third World farmers, about the problems of resistance. At present it is hardly mentioned. All advertising and informational material and all sales contact with farmers should stress that pesticides should be used only when absolutely necessary. Spraying by the calendar, other than in exceptional circumstances, should not be recommended — farmers should be warned that any excess of pesticide use will add to the selection pressure producing resistance. This concept, whereby pesticides permit the resistant proportion of the insect population to increase, is difficult to put across, especially since it may go against the short-term financial interests of individual farmers. It is of such crucial importance, though, that efforts must be made to challenge the 'more must be better' assumption, since the more frequent and persistent the pesticide application the greater is the pressure for the selection of resistant populations.

FAO have produced a model extension leaflet about resistance[47], which could be adapted to the needs of particular Third World countries. The provision of such information and training helps to avoid unnecessary selection pressure for resistance. It can also help farmers and their advisors to anticipate resistance so that substitution, when it is necessary, can take place smoothly. Otherwise, continuing use of chemicals to which resistance has developed may further accentuate the problems.

"Reduction in pesticide pressure provides the most powerful means of reducing the likelihood of resistance crises arising", says Conway.[48] This means not only using pesticides more sensibly, but also in conjunction with other methods:

> "Control relying on a single agent is no longer likely to succeed", says Sawicki. "Relying solely on insecticides can only lead to still more resistance and control problems."[49]

This clearly implies a move towards 'integrated control' or IPM.[50] It must be recognised, however, that this move may be contrary to the short-term financial interests of farmers and to the manufacturers' need for growth in the sales of pesticides. For these reasons, it is a move which is likely to require legislative support. Policies will be needed, internationally, to control pesticide use and to ensure that promotional and informational material concerning pest control or pesticides are consistent with the strategies required to combat resistance.

Malaria control: spraying of houses to eliminate mosquitoes.

27

Pesticides, Malaria and Vector Control

PESTICIDES, MALARIA AND VECTOR CONTROL

"During the night of April 30 I had a chill. It was not severe but I remember huddling deeper into my covers. When I awoke I didn't feel well... Early that afternoon I had a headache and felt uncomfortable... That evening I had a temperature of 102... I awoke the next morning with a temperature of 104.5 and knew I needed medical help... Thursday May 4 is a haze. I know I had fever and chills, and I was probably delirious... The next day I was admitted to a local hospital."[1]

This is part of a description by American naturalist Richard Van Gelder of his experience of malaria. Van Gelder was unlucky enough to pick up the disease on a visit to Africa. The symptoms, chills and fever, enlarged spleen, anaemia, abdominal pains, headaches and lethargy, affect hundreds of millions of Third World people every year. There are no reliable statistics but estimates of the number of malaria cases range between 120 million and 300 million[2] although WHO estimates that only 6.5 million are officially reported.[3] In other worlds, as many as five times the total population of Britain come down with this debilitating disease every year, and perhaps three million of them die, including a million children under 14 in Africa alone.[4] People who live in 'malarious areas' constitute nearly a quarter of the world population. Around a thousand million people are at risk from the disease.[5]

Malaria is only one of a number of diseases which are transmitted by insects. These 'vector-borne' diseases include yellow fever, filariasis (the cause of river blindness and elephantiasis), trypanosomiasis (the cause of African sleeping sickness and Chagas' disease), and dengue fever.

Because they are transmitted by insects, a potential challenge to the spread of these diseases is through the use of pesticides to kill the insect 'vectors'. Over the last 40 years or so pesticides have become the major means of vector control and the main weapon in the battle against these devastating diseases. This strategy has been enormously successful and millions of lives have been saved. As in agriculture though, resistance has caused serious difficulties. The use of pesticides in agriculture has added considerably to the selection pressure, creating resistance in malaria-carrying mosquitoes, particularly in relation to irrigated cotton cultivation in Central America.[6]

The pesticides used in agriculture often kill some of these mosquitoes, as well as the agricultural target pests. The surviving mosquitoes breed in ditches, ponds

28

and rivers, where their offspring may in their turn be exposed to pesticides at the susceptible larval stage. The more susceptible larvae are killed, while the more resistant ones survive. The adults which finally emerge from this environment may by then have developed some resistance to the pesticides used in malaria control programmes.

The selection pressure exerted by agricultural pesticide use has been one of the causes of a considerable resurgence in the incidence of malaria, though not the sole cause. This resurgence, which was most severe in the late 1960s and early 1970s, wiped out much of the earlier progress which had been made in the battle against malaria. Since the mid 1970s, due to variations in strategy, there has been some recovery, but problems still remain. As in agriculture, the reliance on pesticides has left the anti-malaria effort vulnerable to the impact of resistance. Control of agricultural pesticide use and a more diverse strategy in fighting malaria would help to protect and enhance the proven role of pesticides in reducing the incidence of the disease.

The symptoms of malaria are caused by single-celled organisms called plasmodia. There are four types, but the most common are *Plasmodium vivax* and *Plasmodium falciparum*. The plasmodia enter the human bloodstream through the bite of the *Anopheles* mosquito. The falciparum type is a killer - an average of 10% of sufferers die. The vivax type while killing only 1% or less, is more common and may recur at intervals for up to three years, causing weakness and suffering, and leaving the body prey to other diseases.[7]

The cost to the Third World of many millions of cases of malaria every year is massive. People's lives are beyond monetary valuation, but in addition there are the costs of medical care, loss of income of sufferers, reduced productivity due to weakness, and adverse effects on education and tourism.[8] Malaria is primarily a rural disease and reaches its peak during the warm or rainy seasons just at the time when poor rural people have the most work to do.[9] And so the poor are locked into a vicious cycle of poverty and disease.

Anti-malaria campaigns

During the latter half of the 19th century the role of mosquitoes in malaria transmission was established. The mosquitoes breed in water, where the larvae live and so, prior to World War Two, water management, aimed at interrupting the mosquitoes' breeding cycle, was the main technique of malaria control. Draining swamps, oiling or emptying pools of water and controlling irrigation were methods which achieved some success where they were rigorously applied. Around the turn of the century, for example, these methods helped to cut the death rate from malaria among canal company employees in Panama by 80% in just two years.[10] Though we tend to think of malaria as a tropical disease, it once ranged through many temperate lands as far north as the 60th parallel[11] and even included Britain. It was drainage of swampland which eradicated the disease from the Fenlands in Britain and the Pontine marshes of Italy.[12] Malaria was endemic in marshy districts of Britain until the beginning of the twentieth century, the last indigenous case being recorded in 1911.[13]

After World War Two, with the invention of DDT, hope was born that malaria could be completely eliminated. The method takes advantage of the persistence of DDT and the mosquito's habit of resting on the inside walls of houses after biting its victims. By spraying the walls it was possible to shorten the life of the mosquito and so interrupt the transmission of the disease. In 1955 WHO adopted

29

a global malaria eradication policy based on this chemical technique together with drug treatment of sufferers.

Each national campaign was to take just 8 years, commencing with a 1-2 year preparatory phase to set up systems and carry out surveys. This was to be followed by a 3-4 year attack phase, based on spraying, case detection and treatment, intended to cut malaria incidence to 0.01%. The 3-4 year consolidation phase would mop up remaining reservoirs of disease and end when no cases were discovered for three successive years. Finally there was a maintenance phase of vigilance aimed at preventing reintroduction of malaria. By 1958, the campaign included 76 countries and at the peak of the attack phase in 1961/2 69,500 tonnes of pesticides a year were applied by 130,000 spraymen to 100 million dwellings occupied by 575 million people.[14]

This "most ambitious and largest undertaking in public health history"[15] was initially very successful. It is estimated that the number of cases fell from about 300 million before 1946 to about 120 million in the late 1960s in a population which had doubled in size.[16] In the peak years of the mid 1960s, populations of 100 million a year passed into the 'maintenance phase'. It is estimated that up until 1970, the campaign had prevented 2,000 million malaria cases and saved 15 million lives.[17] Statistics about malaria are necessarily unreliable, since it afflicts predominantly rural Third World people who are out of the reach of much statistics-gathering. Nevertheless, it is clear that the campaign achieved enormous success. Pesticides played a central part in this.

Resurgence

By the mid 1960s, though, setbacks began to occur. Drs. Pant and Gratz say:

> "The year 1965 may well be a landmark in the history of efforts against malaria, since the following year there were reverses in the battle against malaria and by the 1970s many of the gains made had been lost."[18]

In India malaria incidence was down to just 49,000 cases in 1961 (from 75 million or so in the early '50s) but was back to over a million by 1971 and nearly 6.5 million by 1976.[19] In Sri Lanka there were only 18 cases reported in 1963 (down from 2.8 million in 1946), but by 1969 malaria again hit half a million people.[20] In Pakistan from 9,500 cases in 1968, the toll rose to 10 million by 1974.[21] In the Gezira region of the Sudan in 1961 malaria was endemic in 7 out of 16 villages. By 1975 it was endemic in all 16.[22] In Haiti the case load grew from 2,500 in 1968 to 26,000 in 1972[23], while a similar pattern asserted itself in Central America. In El Salvador cases increased from 25,300 in 1969 to 83,300 in 1976, in Honduras from 8,800 in 1973 to 48,800 in 1976 and in Nicaragua from 4,200 in 1973 to 26,200 in 1976.[24] Worldwide, the number of new malaria cases increased by over 230% between 1972 and 1976.[25]

In the final years of the 1970s there has been some recovery. This has been due to the renewal of control efforts which were cut back when the disease appeared to be beaten, and also to the substitution of different insecticides in response to resistance. In India, for example, malaria incidence fell from its 1976 peak to 4.4 million in 1977, 3.84 million in 1978 and 2.7 million in 1979.[26] In Sri Lanka, from half a million in 1969, there was a recovery to about 250,000 by 1977, 70,000 by 1978 and 48,000 by 1979.[27]

So far, this recovery has not been sufficient to regain the position reached in the early to mid-sixties. Some of the problems which caused the resurgence of malaria in the late sixties and early seventies are still with us. Further resurgence is possible as mosquitoes develop resistance to more and more insecticides, as they have already done in Central America.[28]

Several factors have contributed to the resurgence. Firstly, there was over-confidence: dramatic successes led to the assumption that all was well and scarce health resources could safely be diverted to other problems. This led to in-adequate surveillance, reduced spraying programmes and loss of enthusiasm. This undoubtedly played a part in the resurgence in Sri Lanka in the '60s, although it was not the sole problem.[29] Secondly, in many countries the infra-structure needed for the case detection and treatment of the 'consolidation phase' was too weak. Escalating costs and periodic shortages of insecticides also contributed to the resurgence.[30] Another factor has been the creation of new mosquito breeding sites, as a result of development and irrigation projects. This is one of the reasons behind the spread of malaria in the Gezira province of the Sudan[31] and has also played a part in India.[32] Adding poor administration and lack of trained personnel, we have a picture of general underdevelopment which suggests that the eradication programme was too ambitious and failed to take full account of the realities of operating in the rural areas of the Third World. In the words of an expert in Malaysia, "it has now been shown beyond reason-able doubt that malaria eradication is not feasible in endemic countries in the tropics".[33] The concept of eradication has now largely been replaced by the more realistic one of control.

Resistance

The most significant cause of the resurgence of malaria, however, is the resis-tance built up by the mosquitoes to the insecticides which have been relied upon for malaria vector control. A 1976 WHO report explains:

> "Even if all other operational, administrative, financial, social and cultural problems are overcome, resistance will emerge as the final difficulty."[34]

Reporting to the XVth International Congress of Entomology in the same year, Dr. Pal of WHO went still further:

> ".... resistance of vectors to pesticides is the biggest single obstacle in the struggle against vector-borne disease."[35]

By 1980, there were 171 species of insects and mites of medical or veterinary importance resistant to at least one, and often to several, pesticides.[36] This figure has grown from 139 in 1975 and 119 in 1967. There has also been an increase in the number of chemicals involved. In 1978 there were 51 resistant species of *Anopheles* mosquitoes (the ones which carry malaria), an increase of 9 over 1975. Of these 51 species, 34 were resistant to DDT, 47 to dieldrin, 30 to both DDT and dieldrin, 10 to organophosphates and 4 to carbamates. The Central American malaria vector *Anopheles albimanus* showed resistance to insecticides of *all* these classes.

Once resistance to organophosphates begins there is a strong tendency to cross-resistance so that other species could well develop the same kind of multiple resistance as *A. albimanus*. A similar pattern is emerging among the culcine mosquitoes which carry filariasis and dengue fever. Even resistance to the new

31

pyrethroids has been reported, for example, in *A. arabiensis* in the Sudan and *A. stephensi* in Pakistan. By 1975, in 14 countries for which information was available, the total population of areas affected by resistance in malaria vectors was more than 256 million, about a third of the total population of malarious areas in those countries.[37]

So resistance by vector insects, especially malaria carrying mosquitoes, threatens the health and livelihoods of millions of poor Third World people. It is also very expensive. When resistance develops, the response is usually to switch to another chemical. But replacing DDT with malathion increases costs as much as 7 times, while using the carbamate propoxur increases costs by up to 27 times.[38] In Central America alone it was estimated in 1977 that the cost of increased resistance, not to mention the suffering and the lives lost, amounted to about £7 million a year.[39] In poor countries this extra expense can lead to continued use of the less effective chemicals and reductions in the effectiveness of malaria control. There is no doubt that resistance causes more people to contract the disease and is a major factor in its resurgence.

The 5th report of the WHO Expert Committee on Vector Biology and Control, published in 1980, summarised the current position:

".... the steady development of resistance to an increasing number of insecticides by an increasing number of vector species over wider geographical areas has impeded disease control programmes in many countries... The above difficulties relate primarily to the change in insecticides used in malaria control programmes, from the long-lasting and relatively low-cost organochlorines to the organo-phosphate and carbamate compounds, which not only are more expensive to manufacture, but also require more frequent application. Thus, expenditure on vector control has greatly increased, and... the cost... in many countries is reaching or exceeding the levels acceptable to governments."[40]

Even if a country can afford to respond to resistance by changing to a new insecticide, this can only provide temporary relief at considerable expense. In the words of Dr. Pant of WHO:

"In 10 years time a US scientist in his laboratory will invent a new insecticide, yet somewhere in an Asian swamp is a mosquito today which already possesses the gene to resist it."[41]

In order to see how resistance can be avoided, and control continued despite it, it is necessary to look at the causes of resistance. Although the use of pesti-cides in the malaria control programmes themselves exerts some selection pressure on the mosquitoes, this is not great. Because vector control pesticides are sprayed inside houses, they affect only a small proportion of the mosquito population, and only adults. More and more evidence is accumulating from around the world that it is the use of pesticides in agriculture which exerts the most dramatic selection pressure on the mosquitoes. More pesticides are used in agriculture than for vector control.[42] This agricultural pesticide use affects a greater proportion of the mosquito population and exposes the mosquitoes to pesticides at the susceptible larval stage. This leads to the more rapid develop-ment of resistance and the consequent resurgence of malaria. Insofar as pesticide use in agriculture is excessive or uncontrolled, it may be unnecessarily subjecting millions of people to the risk of malaria.

The relationship between agricultural spraying and vector resistance has been demonstrated by the impact of crop spraying on mosquito populations, by fluctuations in mosquito resistance related to the time and intensity of crop spraying, and by the correspondence between the spectrum of mosquito resistance and the types of insecticides used in agriculture. Agricultural insecticide use has also killed off the mosquitoes' natural enemies.[43]

Since pesticides used in malaria control programmes are sprayed inside people's houses there is a particularly crucial need for safety. For this reason a chemical is only accepted for this use after years of exhaustive tests. In agriculture though, the use of insecticides in the Third World is subject to very few effective controls. This means that a pesticide may be used in agriculture, and exerting selection pressure on the mosquitoes, for years before it is approved for vector control. By that time resistance may already be developing and the usefulness of the pesticide for vector control will be jeopardised. Also, the selection pressure already exerted on mosquitoes by a wide range of agricultural insecticides appears to increase the likelihood that the mosquitoes will very quickly develop resistance to a new chemical. For all these reaons, says Professor Georghiou of the University of California,

> "Mosquito resistance of a level sufficient to impede their control
> has been most severe in areas where crops are treated frequently
> with insecticides".[44]

Table 2 lists cases where resistance has been linked to agricultural pesticide use. This includes 12 species of *Anopheles* mosquitoes in 20 Third World countries.

In Central America, the extra costs in malaria control, resulting from resistance, have been described as "perhaps the most significant economic consequence of pesticide use in cotton".[45] Even so, the resistance still leads to more cases of malaria. In Guatemala, ICAITI (the Central American Research Institute for Industry) estimates that a 10% increase in resistance leads to a 7.5% increase in malaria rates, while an increase of 1% in the area planted with cotton may result in an increase in malaria of 136 cases per million of population.[46]

Problems in Chemical Vector Control

The toll of sickness and death from malaria and the cycle of poverty and disease associated with it are, in many parts of the world, indirectly worsened as a result of the uncontrolled use of pesticides in agriculture. Greater controls on the trade in pesticides and on their marketing and use are an essential measure in any future attempts to control malaria. Measures to reduce reliance on chemicals for the management of agricultural pests can contribute to better health for the Third World's poor in this way, as well as leading to better crops, fewer cases of poisoning and a safer environment.

Safer, more effective and better controlled use of pesticides in agriculture can help to preserve the effectiveness of pesticides for vector control, but even in vector control, excessive reliance on the chemical strategy can lead to problems. Firstly, these pesticides also contribute to resistance and so their use should be kept to the minimum consistent with effective vector control. Secondly, DDT used for malaria control contributes about 8% of total global DDT contamination.[47] Thirdly, the use of pesticides in malaria control can have an undesirable impact on non-target organisms. In the Sierra Madre Occidental

Table 2

Cases of Resistance to Insecticides in Mosquitoes Precipitated by Indirect Selection Pressure by Agricultural Insecticides

SPECIES	COUNTRY	CROP	INSECTICIDE RESISTANCE
Anopheles acconitus	Java	various crops, rice	dieldrin, DDT
A. albimanus	El Salvador, Nicaragua	cotton, rice	parathion me. parathion malathion fenitrothion propoxur carbaryl
	Mexico, Guatemala, El Salvador, Honduras, Nicaragua	cotton	DDT dieldrin
A. culcifacaes	India (A.P. & Haryana)		malathion
A. gambiae s.1.	Ivory Coast	coffee, cacao	dieldrin
	Nigeria	ground nuts	dieldrin
	Ghana	cacao	dieldrin
	Mali	cotton	dieldrin
	Upper Volta	cotton	DDT
	Sudan, Ethiopia, Togo, Senegal	various crops	DDT
A. maculipennis	Romania, Turkey	crops	dieldrin
A. melanoon subalpinus	Turkey	crops	dieldrin
A. melas	Zaire	bananas	DDT
A. pharoensis	Egypt	cotton	dieldrin, DDT
	Sudan	various crops	dieldrin, DDT
A. quadrimaculatus	USA	cotton	dieldrin
	Mexico	cotton	DDT, dieldrin
A. rufipes	Mali	cotton	dieldrin
A. sacharovi	Greece, Turkey	cotton, rice	DDT, dieldrin
A. sinensis	China	rice	OC & OP
Aedes aegypti	Tahiti	coconut	dieldrin
Aedes nigromaculis	USA	various crops	DDT, dieldrin, OP
Culex pipiens fatigans	USA	various crops	OP

Sources. George P. Georghiou, "The Implication of Agricultural Insecticides in the Development of Resistance by Mosquitoes" in *The Agromedical Approach to Pesticide Management,* UC/AID, 1976, pp. 34-35.

WHO, Resistance of Vectors of Disease to Pesticides: Fifth Report of the WHO Expert Committee on Vector Biology and Control, Technical Report Series 655, WHO, Geneva, 1980, pp. 16 & 19.

of Mexico, for example, periodic spraying against malaria has led to the death of house cats and a consequent explosion in the rat population.

"With the increased loss of stored corn due to the rats" says Dr. David Werner, "the economic and nutritional status of the people is substantially lowered."[48]

The fourth problem concerns safety. Bad storage conditions and insufficient quality control can increase the hazard of malathion used in malaria control programmes. The addition of poor working practices sets the scene for poisoning incidents such as that in Pakistan in 1976 when some 2,500 malaria control workers were poisoned.[49]

WHO says that malathion is safe for malaria control, provided protective clothing is regularly cleaned and a high standard of personal hygiene is maintained. These conditions are not always fulfilled. Other chemicals now being used for malaria control include fenitrothion and propoxur, which WHO describes as "at the limit of acceptable toxicity for conventional indoor application". Strict precautionary measures must be adhered to in the use of these chemicals, it says.[50]

Integrated Vector Control

For all these reasons it is essential that non-chemical methods of vector control be given greater attention. The engineering and water management techniques which were relied upon before the DDT era must be revived and take their place alongside pesticides in a more integrated form of vector control which can involve Third World communities actively in the battle against disease. Less dependence on chemicals for vector control must go hand in hand with better pesticide management in agriculture in order to make the most effective use of the few pesticides which are suitable in the campaign against the malaria mosquito. Also, development and irrigation projects must be designed with their vector control implications clearly in mind.

One useful tactic is to restrict certain pesticides to vector control use only. In Sri Lanka, health and agricultural authorities have agreed that malathion will not be used for agricultural purposes. So far this seems to be working, although cross-resistance may arise from other organophosphates still used in agriculture. It is also necessary, therefore, to control all agricultural pesticide use and to use all available non-chemical vector control methods.

The Sarvodaya Shramadana Movement and the Anti-Malaria Campaign in Sri Lanka in consultation with OXFAM America, are planning an experimental malaria control campaign, assisted by some funding from OXFAM. The programme will be based on the participation of villagers in eliminating the mosquitoes' breeding sites. The first stage of the programme will be research, based on 40 villages, designed to explore the impact of popular participation. It will also seek to find out whether traditional health practices influence the prevalence of malaria and how these practices could be integrated into the malaria control programme.

Half the villages will be the subject of a joint programme between Sarvodaya and the Anti-Malaria Campaign which will test the impact of greater community participation on a programme based on spraying houses and drug treatment of malaria cases. In the other 20 villages case treatment will be combined with community control of breeding sites but without spraying. It will also be possible to compare these two groups of villages with others receiving the standard services of the Anti-Malaria Campaign.

If the methods tested prove successful, then malaria prevention programmes will be undertaken throughout Sri Lanka, taking advantage of Sarvodaya's existing work in 3,000 villages.[51] This kind of programme would represent an important development initiative in which malaria prevention and control was based on working with the poor at village level, rather than applying an imported technology without their active participation.

This scheme is currently only in the planning stage and it remains, for the time being, a good idea which has yet to become reality. Similar measures, though, have already achieved considerable success in China, where villagers have been mobilised to fill in holes and pits where mosquitoes breed, to drain ditches and to divert stagnant water.[52] In other places *Gambusia* and *Poecilia* fish have been used to feed on the mosquito larvae.[53] This method is also a part of a community participation vector control project operating in eight coastal villages in Pondicherry, South India.[54] This kind of community based programme may also be able to take greater advantage of personal protection from the mosquito, for example by the use of mosquito nets.

* * * * * *

In 1976 the WHO Expert Committee on Insecticides looked at resistance problems in vector control. This was their final conclusion:

"The committee was convinced of the important role of heavy and regular applications of pesticides in inducing resistance and noted that this was most likely to occur as a result of agricultural use... It was therefore recommended that via the existing collaboration between WHO and FAO, steps be taken to advise member governments to monitor the import, manufacture, marketing and use of all pesticides so that some warning can be given of possible future development of resistance. Wherever possible, regulations should be introduced to control the entry and use of such pesticides."[55]

The use of pesticides for the control of malaria has saved many lives. There is no question of advocating the complete withdrawal of pesticides from public health use, where their role is largely beneficial. That beneficial role, however, would be prolonged and enhanced through the adoption of resistance-avoiding strategies. This would entail more careful use of pesticides, in combination with other methods, in integrated vector control programmes. It would also require that appropriate controls are exercised over the use of pesticides in agriculture in malarious areas.

While these measures depend largely on the actions of Third World governments, there is also an opportunity for positive action by the governments and manufacturers in the pesticide-exporting countries. Importing countries should receive the fullest information about the health and environmental characteristics of the products they are buying and be sure that these are of good quality. International action should be taken to ensure that pesticides are not promoted in such a way as may result in their being used excessively or wrongly, thus giving rise to unnecessary selection pressure on mosquitoes and consequent suffering or death from malaria.

36

Occupational and Accidental Poisoning

OCCUPATIONAL AND ACCIDENTAL POISONING

José Luis, his wife Maria and their five children make their way, every year between November and March, to the Pacific plains of Guatemala. They are typical of the hundreds of thousands of people who migrate from the hill country to the coastal plains annually to harvest coffee, cotton and sugar. There they are exposed to appalling living conditions and to pesticides and malaria. During their months in the cotton fields, many of these people will suffer the ill-effects of pesticide poisoning.[1]

Most of the poisoning cases are caused by organophosphate pesticides. An American specialist describes the symptoms:

"Symptoms usually come on between 2-4 hours after skin exposure and 15-60 minutes after ingestion... The muscarinic effects include nausea, vomiting, abdominal cramps, involuntary defecation, diarrhoea, sweating, salivation, pain in the chest and a blurring of vision... The nicotinic effects include weakness, fasciculations, twitching and flaccid paralysis. The patient is anxious, restless and may soon develop convulsions and coma. When seen early he is pale, sweating, frothing at the mouth."[2]

Death due to respiratory failure can result. In the case of parathion (one of the most acutely toxic organophosphates), for example, "an oral dose of 3-5 mg/kg is reported to be usually fatal to man".[3] This means, for a 70 kg man, a dose of 210-350 mg, about a quarter of a gram or one-hundredth of an ounce.

In 1972 the WHO's Expert Committee on Insecticides estimated that there were about 500,000 cases of accidental pesticide poisoning annually.[4] The Committee estimated that about 1% of these cases resulted in death in countries "where medical treatment and antidotes are readily available" but possibly higher in other countries. This estimate was reached by constructing a model based on available statistics from 19 countries. The estimate was "made on a rather conservative basis".

'The actual model suggested that about 9,200 deaths occurred per annum and that the number of cases was about 500,000, but that the limits of error were 250,000-1,453,000."[5]

Third World countries probably account for about half the poisoning cases.[6] Based on the world total of 500,000 cases and 9,200 deaths, our calculations

37

suggest that there would be some 250,000 cases in Third World countries, with 6,700 deaths.[7] Thus, in 1972 Third World people, with less than 15% of pesticide consumption, may have suffered half of the cases of accidental pesticide poisoning and nearly three-quarters of the deaths from this cause.

Since 1972 the real growth in the world pesticide market has been estimated to be around 5% per annum.[8] At this rate pesticide use would have increased by about 50% by 1980/81. If pesticide poisoning cases are assumed to have increased at the same rate, we would have by 1981 an annual rate of 750,000 with 13,800 deaths. In the Third World there would be 375,000 cases with some 10,000 deaths a year. This estimate is based on an initial figure which is considered to be a conservative one.[9]

In short, no accurate and reliable figures are available, but estimates indicate a problem of considerable magnitude. In addition, these estimates do not include any of the chronic and long-term health effects of pesticides. The cancers, birth defects, sterility and so on which constitute some of the most widely publicised concerns about pesticide use, especially in the rich countries, do not register in these figures. In the Third World pesticides are often used in suicide attempts. The many deaths and injuries which result are also excluded from the WHO figures.

While there is a legitimate cause for concern over these pesticides having possibly harmful long-term consequences, the more immediate health problem in the Third World is that of acute poisoning, where sickness or death occur rapidly from exposure over a short period of time. These cases affect men, women and children in many countries and this chapter will look in more detail at some of these countries.

Pesticide poisoning cases in the Third World occur in a variety of ways. Farm workers mixing and applying these chemicals or entering fields after spraying are the group most at risk. Other people, working in formulation factories or for anti-malaria programmes, may also be exposed in the course of their work. It has been estimated that around 40% of accidental poisonings are occupational.[10] Other cases include children drinking pesticides by mistake, families using pesticide containers for storing food or water, and the contamination of food during transport or storage. In all these cases, the common cause is the availability, often with very little effective restriction or control, of very toxic pesticides in conditions where the necessary safety precautions are highly unrealistic. Dr. Copplestone of WHO has said that,

> "In all societies, but especially where literacy is low, probably the
> most effective single measure to promote safety is restriction of
> the availability of the more toxic pesticides to those who have been
> trained in their use, and who have a specific need to use them".[11]

In most Third World societies the number of people who have the training and equipment for safe use of the more toxic pesticides is relatively small. Yet many of these pesticides, restricted on safety grounds in the rich countries, are freely available in the poor, where the risks are greatest.

The combination of heat, malnutrition and the burden of disease makes Third World farm workers and their families especially susceptible to the hazards of pesticides.

> "Well nourished, comfortably housed workers, enjoying adequate

rest and hygiene, are less vulnerable to toxic chemicals than persons who are burdened with malnutrition, disease and fatigue", says ILO's *Guide to Health and Hygiene in Agricultural Work.*[12]

Yet the Third World farm worker is usually denied access to the protective clothing which in rich countries is accepted as essential for the safe use of pesticides. Even where protective clothing is available, the poor cannot afford to buy it and the heat makes it almost impossible to wear, except for short periods in the cooler part of the day, or at altitudes where temperatures are milder.

In addition, the small Third World farmer has little access to independent information about the correct use of pesticides. Extension services of poor countries are usually inadequate and stretched to the limit of their meagre resources.

These countries also have immense problems in creating effective legislation to control the import, formulation and sale of pesticides. They have many problems to deal with and few resources. They lack the facilities to test and monitor the nature and quality of pesticides, or to carry out tests to examine their behaviour under specific climatic conditions. They cannot afford the people to police legislation and inspect factories and shops. Communications are poor, corruption exists and the power of vested interests is great. For all these reasons very few Third World countries have comprehensive and well-enforced pesticide legislation. A recent survey by FAO found 81 countries for which no information existed concerning measures to control pesticides, or in which such measures were known not to exist.[13]

These are some of the factors which add to the special hazards involved in pesticide use in the Third World. The 'hazard' is the real risk to health and must take account of the volume of use, the protection available and the susceptibility of the person as well as the toxicity of the product. Toxicity is usually determined on the basis of the effect on test animals of an amount of pesticide entering the body by one of a number of routes — through the mouth (oral), the skin (dermal) or by inhalation. Oral and dermal toxicities are expressed by the term 'LD_{50}'. This is the dose which results in the death of 50% of the test animals, usually rats, and this dose is expressed in milligrams per kilogram of the animal's body weight. Different animals may be more or less susceptible. Humans, for example, may be more or less susceptible than rats. The figures we will use, unless otherwise specified, are the oral LD_{50} in the rat. Since most occupational exposure is through the skin, though, the dermal LD_{50} is often a better indicator of the hazard of a product in use.

The LD_{50} figures and the WHO classification of pesticides by hazard[14] (to which we will often refer) relate to the 'technical compound'. This is the form of the active ingredient from which actual pesticide formulations are made. Different formulations of the same active ingredient may have different properties and some formulations contain more than one active ingredient. The formulation describes the way the ingredients are made up for sale and use. It includes the percentage of each active ingredient, its physical state (eg liquid, powder, granules) and the way in which it will be mixed prior to application (eg water-wettable powder (WP), emulsifiable concentrate(EC)). Granular formulations with a low percentage of active ingredient are less dangerous than high percentage liquids or powders. Their effectiveness for pest control will vary too, of course.

39

The pesticides which are the direct cause of poisoning in the Third World are often manufactured in the rich world. Certain of them are either banned in their countries of origin, their uses restricted, or their use only permitted by operators who are supplied with appropriate protection. The pesticides most commonly responsible for poisoning cases in the Third World include parathion, mevinphos, endrin, dieldrin and pentachlorophenol (PCP).[15]

In 1976 approximately 30% of US pesticide exports were of products whose use was prohibited in the USA.[16] Perhaps the most notorious example is the pesticide leptophos, marketed under the brand name Phosvel. Leptophos is classified by WHO as "extremely hazardous" on the basis of delayed neuro-toxicity - it can cause paralysis some time after exposure. Leptophos was implicated in the death of 1,300 water buffalo in Egypt in 1971 and in further poisoning incidents of animals and people in 1973 and 1974.[17] Leptophos was given only temporary registration in the US in 1971. Since the early seventies it has been sold in a number of Third World countries. In 1976 it became public that workers at the US factory were suffering nervous disorders — they were called the 'Phosvel Zombies'. After this the plant was closed, but the product continued to circulate, and to be banned, in one country after another. As Velsicol, the manufacturers of Phosvel, point out, such sales may have been carried out by third parties not subject to their control. Leptophos was banned in Colombia in 1977, and was voluntarily withdrawn by Velsicol from the market in the Philippines in 1978. In 1978 it turned up in Costa Rica and, although no longer manufactured, it was recently reported on sale in Indonesia. In 1980 Phosvel was reported as available in Antigua.[18]

In response to an approach by OXFAM, Velsicol stated:

"From our own investigations in Egypt, we were not able to turn up conclusive evidence that would support these allegations".

Velsicol also stated that inventories of Phosvel in Indonesia were recalled and destroyed in 1977, and that products subsequently distributed under the Phosvel name in Indonesia are not Phosvel. The company concluded that, "where any Phosvel stock is discovered and is under our control, we will carry out an environmentally acceptable disposal program of such material from anywhere in the world".[19]

Not only are various hazardous pesticides, restricted in their countries of origin, often freely available in the Third World, but they are often sold with labels giving incomplete safety information. The information which is given is often not in the local language of the area and anyway, in most Third World countries, few people are able to read in any language. Pesticides are often packed in quantities which necessitate re-packing at the retail level with consequent dangers of exposure and lack of labels for the final user. Finally, these pesticides may be advertised and promoted in such a way as to give an erroneous impression of their safety.[20]

In the Third World illiteracy, lack of training and equipment, lack of effective legislative controls, and an especially susceptible population combine with the availability of highly toxic pesticides which are often badly labelled, poorly packaged and irresponsibly promoted. In addition, the pressures of the treadmill may drive people to apply pesticides more often and in greater quantities than is desirable either for maximum safety or for the best crop yields. The result of all these factors is the regular and widespread incidence of poisoning. This can be effectively demonstrated by looking in more depth at the problems in some particular countries and regions.

Ian Haynes

Bad storage practice in a local pesticide store in Africa. Lack of labels, open sacks, and illegible instructions are likely to lead to misuse of pesticides.

Central America

In the four Central American countries of Guatemala, El Salvador, Honduras and Nicaragua (combined population 15 million) investigations found 14,138 cases of pesticide poisoning from 1972 to 1975, including 40 deaths.[21] The actual numbers were probably much higher. A nurse in Guatemala said, in 1977 at the peak of the spraying season:

> "At this time of year, we treat 30 or 40 people a day for pesticide poisoning. The farmers often tell the peasants to give another reason for their sickness, but you can smell the pesticide in their clothes."[22]

Doctors, priests and peasant leaders believe that numerous unreported deaths take place each year. And, indeed, in 1972 a Ministry of Labour survey in El Salvador found 6 times as many deaths as indicated by data collected from hospitals.[23] "Some of the large cotton producers maintain their own private clinics", says the ICAITI report. The purpose of these clinics is partly "to hinder public health officials from detecting the seriousness of human insecticide poisonings".[24]

Apart from under-reporting, the relatively low proportion of deaths to poisoning cases is related to the circumstances in which pesticide poisoning usually occurs in Central America: workers harvesting cotton or examining plants for pests (scouts) enter the fields after spraying; their skin brushes against the pesticide-soaked plants and they suffer from mild poisoning. Most of these cases are never reported and if symptoms become more severe the workers stay away from the fields until they recover. Thus, the pattern is of repeated mild or moderate episodes of poisoning, only rarely resulting in death. This pattern also militates against a realistic assessment of the incidence of poisoning.

It has been seen in Chapters 1 and 2 how Central America has suffered from treadmill crises leading to unusually heavy pesticide applications. The consequences for health are especially serious because many of the people who work in the cotton fields are temporary labourers living in appalling conditions. Three quarters of people interviewed in the cotton-growing areas were insufficiently literate to read warnings and instructions about pesticide use, and many could not speak Spanish, the official language of the Central American region. Many were undernourished, and housing for temporary workers normally had no walls and therefore no protection against spray.[25] Almost all workers lived within 100 metres of the cotton fields.[26] Most of the workers exposed to pesticides had no access to protective clothing; 60% of houses had no toilet and 75% no running water.[27] The availability of washing facilities is one of the basic essentials of pesticide safety. In the absence of these facilities, workers often have to wash in the irrigation channels which contain pesticide residues and can add to their exposure rather than reducing it.[28]

Three years after the publication of the second edition of the ICAITI report, OXFAM contacts in Guatemala reported that some of the most dangerous of all pesticides were still freely available. The Social Security Institute (IGSS) reported at least ten deaths from pesticide poisoning in Guatemala in 1979. Although technicians have access to protective clothing, the hired labourers who are the usual victims do not. Pesticides are still widely advertised by such means as radio spots and billboards. Agronomist José Ponciano, who works for the Information and Training Section of the Mediterranean Fly Project in Guatemala, says that marketing practices are not consistent with sensible pesticide use.

> "The sales representatives and the companies are interested in sales. The use [by farmers] of pesticides is often irrational. Few people have proper technical assistance."[29]

In most countries no reliable statistics on the incidence of pesticide poisoning are kept and so information is restricted to occasional surveys or reports of major incidents. Two of these from other parts of Central America and the

Caribbean serve to illustrate the problems.

The Director of Trinidad and Tobago's Bureau of Standards, Dr. M.G. Lines, reported 293 confirmed poisoning cases during 1978 and 1979 out of a population of only just over a million.[30] In the Comarca Lagunera district of northern Mexico in 1974, there was an outbreak of pesticide poisoning involving 847 cases, including 4 deaths. According to a study published in 1975 most (92.5%) of the cases were due to inhalation of the pesticides, especially Mevidrin (a formulation of the highly toxic ingredients mevinphos and monocrotophos[31]) methyl parathion, and Sevin (a formulation of carbaryl — usually considered only moderately hazardous).[32]

Sri Lanka

The extent of the pesticide problem in Sri Lanka was revealed when we spoke to farmers in the Teldeniya area in 1980. Most farmers had some personal experience of the toxic effects of pesticides. In the small village of Wewagama, they had many problems. The Rambanda family, for example, had just an acre of land to support the six of them. There was a water shortage. In September 1980 the villagers were harvesting their tomatoes. They explained that they often felt faint when they sprayed their fields — they just rested until they felt better. There is no protective clothing to be had for these poor farmers and so it is important that they get full and correct advice about the importance of using pesticides of low toxicity, warnings of hazards and methods of avoiding them. Instead, the extension services are stretched and some very hazardous chemicals, such as parathion and methamidophos, are freely available.

The son of the Rambandas' neighbour spent four days in hospital in 1979 with pesticide poisoning. He was one of many. Others, though, do not even associate their symptoms with pesticides. Mr Sananayake, for example, said at first that he felt no ill-effects from spraying the herbicide, paraquat. But when asked if he suffered from nose-bleeds he admitted that he did. He did not realise that this is a symptom of paraquat inhalation.

The experiences of these small farmers indicate that there are probably many cases of minor poisoning, and perhaps some major ones,which do not register in the statistics. These statistics are compiled on the basis of the number of cases which reach Sri Lanka's hospitals and are correctly diagnosed.

Many of the cases admitted to hospitals in Sri Lanka are the result of suicide attempts. The figures for accidental and occupational poisoning constitute something like 30% of the total number of cases.[33]

In 1978, 15,504 people were admitted to government hospitals with pesticide poisoning; 1,029 of them died. The situation in the two previous years was not significantly different.

These dramatic figures indicate that, from a population of only just over 14 million, two and a half times as many people are hospitalised for pesticide poisoning as in the US and nearly five times as many die.[34] This despite the fact that the US uses about a third of all the pesticides in the world — perhaps twice as much as all Third World countries combined. If we include only the accidental cases in Sri Lanka, the figure is still more than two-thirds that of the US, with probably a greater number of deaths.

Table 3
Pesticide Poisoning Cases Admitted
to Government Hospitals, Sri Lanka 1975-78

YEAR	CASES	DEATHS
1975	13,648	1,042
1976	13,778	964
1977	14,653	938
1978	15,504	1,029

Sources: J. Jeyeratnam, "Planning for the health of the worker", SLAAS Theme Seminar, Annual Session, 1979.
J. Jeyeratnam, "Health hazards awareness of pesticide applicators about pesticides", in E.A.H.van Heemstra and W.F. Tordoir (eds), *Education and Safe Handling in Pesticide Application*, Elsevier, Amsterdam, 1982, p.24.

These figures also indicate that the scale of accidental pesticide poisoning in Sri Lanka is even more severe than that in Central America, which has caused considerable concern and has served to focus the debate in the US on the pesticide problems of the Third World.

Dr. J. Jeyeratnam, when head of the Department of Community Medicine at the Faculty of Medicine in Colombo, made a study of the pesticide poisoning problem in Sri Lanka. He points out that Sri Lanka's national average of 104.5 cases per 100,000 of population is "probably the highest in the world, as determined from available published data". In one region, Vavuniya, in the far northeast of Sri Lanka, the rate in 1977 was 381.2 and in neighbouring Jaffna, 342.2. Even excluding the cases of intentional poisoning, these are very high figures.[35]

"The magnitude of the problem can be viewed in correct perspective," says Jeyeratnam, "when one considers it in relation to other national health problems." For example, in 1977, the number of deaths from pesticide poisoning far exceeded those from malaria, tetanus, diphtheria, whooping cough and polio combined.

Table 4
Deaths from Pesticide Poisoning and Some
Communicable Diseases, Sri Lanka, 1977

Malaria	2
Tetanus	604
Diphtheria	17
Whooping Cough	6
Poliomyelitis	17
TOTAL	*646* Pesticide poisoning *938*

Source: J. Jeyeratnam, "Planning for the health of the worker", SLAAS Theme Seminar, Annual Session, 1979.

Many of these cases, as we have seen, are suicidal, but the significance of occupational poisoning is confirmed by a follow-up study made by Jeyeratnam in

1978. In Kegalle district alone, between Colombo and Kandy, during the 'yala' (April-August) season of 1978, there were an estimated 1,021 poisoning episodes. This poisoning outbreak was strongly associated with an attack of the brown planthopper rice pest, and a detailed study of 23 cases showed that these were paddy farmers poisoned while spraying their fields.[36]

Almost a year later, 19 of these spraymen were traced and 9 of them revealed symptoms such as sweating, salivation and muscle cramps. Only one of these was continuing to spray. In all 23 cases the patients either had leaky sprayers or had sprayed against the wind, but they were also using extremely dangerous chemicals, such as parathion which cannot be safely used in a Third World country where protective clothing is neither available nor practical, and where knowledge of pesticide hazards is low and equipment often of a poor standard. A number of the pesticides involved in these 23 cases are still freely available in Sri Lanka, and also in many other Third World countries. These include parathion (Folidol), and methamidophos (Tamaron). Also, at least 7 of these spraymen had been using Endrex 20, a formulation produced by Shell associates, Lankem. The trade name Endrex was used in Sri Lanka prior to 1976/7 for a formulation containing the active ingredient endrin, an organochlorine. Subsequently, however, the same name has been applied to at least two different formulations, containing different active ingredients. The formulation implicated in the poisoning cases in 1978 was found to contain a mixture of aldrin (an organochlorine) and ethyl parathion (a highly toxic organophosphate). Such a mixture "may cause problems in providing appropriate therapy".[37]

In 1981 the name Endrex was used for a mixture of diazinon and methyl parathion. Such changes in active ingredients under a single brand name could cause problems both for doctors and for farmers. In this case the problems were accentuated by the failure of the company, Lankem, to alter the medical advice on the label until some three months after the initial change in active ingredient.

Shell have since stated that the brand name Endrex "will not be used in future insecticide products in Sri Lanka", and they are satisfied that such an incident could not happen again. They have in addition agreed to consider sending a strong advisory note to all associate companies asking for notification of any proposed changes in formulations.[38]

In 1980 a report on health and safety in pesticide formulation factories in Sri Lanka was given to an ILO seminar in Colombo. Here are some quotations from that report:

> "There are a few other deaths which on investigation revealed exposure of the victims to pesticides in one or other of the factories formulating pesticides."

> "... In all pesticide work, the greatest hazard lies in the handling of concentrates. In transferring concentrates from drums either threaded taps or drum taps of standard design should be usually used. However, this practice is not strictly followed in most of our factories."

> "... devices for exhaust ventilation have been installed forgetting the fundamentals of occupational safety and health engineering and thus defeating the purpose of installation of such systems. Hence in our formulation factories the environment, the materials... and the man -- the worker and his clothes — are subjected to contamina-

tion by pesticides... The conditions may differ only in degrees but remain the same in most of our factories."

"... In all the factories adequate protective clothing is not provided to the workers."

"... The workers of two formulating factories are biologically monitored once a week. The exposure level of workers to organophosphorous pesticides are such that about 50% of them show prounounced reduction of blood cholinesterase activity.[39] In this connection it is regrettable to note the following phrases from a letter addressed to an employee by an employer: 'The purpose of this letter is to advise you that unless we notice a remarkable improvement in your blood cholinesterase activity within the ensuing 3 months period, the company will be left with no option but to terminate your services'."[40]

The major formulation factories in Sri Lanka are associated with UK-based companies, Shell and ICI, and the German company Bayer, although there are also a number of other plants and it is not known at which factory the above incident occurred.

We have approached these three European companies. Shell have accepted that, in the past, conditions in the Lankem plant were not adequate. They state, though, that the conditions described no longer apply.[41]

ICI have responded that:

"There have been no severe or chronic problems ... CIC's [ICI's Sri Lankan associate] employees are certainly not put at risk in their occupation ... There is little likelihood of problems at the docks or in transport ... CIC do not transfer pesticide concentrates by hand ... The plant has been designed with full dust extraction ... the equipment in the CIC factory has been designed to UK safety standards ... Proper protective clothing is provided to the workers in CIC."[42]

Bayer have informed us that they have undertaken "an immediate check" regarding conditions in the Sri Lanka formulation plant of their associate Haychem.[43]

Most occupational poisoning cases in Sri Lanka appear to affect cultivators of rice and vegetables. These are not rich farmers. Over 90% of the 600,000 paddy (rice) holdings are of 10 acres or less.[44] It is among the mass of the rural poor in this poor country that pesticides take their toll. While recent legislation restricts the import of certain chemicals, many potentially hazardous ones were still freely available late in 1980. Out of 36 insecticides on the Formulary list of permitted pesticides[45] four are restricted by the US Environmental Protection Agency (aldrin, BHC, chlordane and ethyl parathion), 9 are covered, in Britain, by Health and Safety Regulations requiring the use of protective clothing (carbofuran, chlorfenvinphos, demeton-S-methyl, dichlorvos, endosulfan, methomyl, omethoate, parathion and phosphamidon), and aldrin and chlordane are restricted in the EEC under Directive 79/117/EEC. Of the 36, 12 are classified by WHO as "extremely hazardous" or "highly hazardous".

On a visit by the author to a shop in a small town near Colombo in September 1980, none of the bottles of pesticide seen gave any recommendations regarding protective clothing, without which it is virtually impossible to use the more toxic products safely. They did not even indicate that long trousers, long-sleeved shirt, wide-brimmed hat, and footwear would help — these are the minimum safety requirements for any pesticide. The shopkeeper, though conscientious, had no special qualifications, yet was often called upon by farmers to recommend chemicals. The UN Economic and Social Commission for Asia and the Pacific (ESCAP) have set up an imaginative scheme to use shopkeepers as a major channel of information to farmers about safety and pest control. ARSAP (Agricultural Requisites Scheme for Asia and the Pacific) holds workshops for government personnel in various countries who will then be able to arrange training courses for the retailers.[46] This is a valuable initiative, though of course it needs to be supplemented by proper control and labelling of pesticides.

Another widespread problem in Sri Lanka, as in other Third World countries, concerns the quality of pesticide application equipment. Sprayers are expensive and old ones continue in use even though they may be leaky and poorly maintained. Sprayers can be hired from the government extension service, but better-off villagers who own sprayers also hire them out, often with workers to do the spraying. These contract spraymen are paid by the acre and so often work as much as ten hours a day, despite the fact that poisoning through the skin is most likely in the heat of the day. Indeed, in the summer of 1980, 67 spraymen are reported to have died in the Polonnaruwa area.[47]

Poor use practices contribute greatly to the hazards in Sri Lanka as elsewhere. Educational programmes (like ARSAP) could help to improve these, and advertisements and labels could be seen as a part of the educational process and devised accordingly. Even so, it is difficult to follow good practices when highly toxic products are freely available, but good equipment is lacking or beyond the means of farmers.

Although Sri Lanka's new legislation may help a little, it remains an unknown quantity and enforcement will not be easy. Other factors are likely to make the problem worse not better. Increasing resistance problems lead growers to use potentially lethal high doses of 'cocktails' of pesticides; the brown planthopper problem (partly the result of pesticide use in the first place) shows no immediate signs of abating, although the Sri Lankans are working on resistant varieties of rice. Most importantly perhaps, the massive Mahaweli Development Scheme will bring 600,000 acres of new land into cultivation some of it perhaps growing cotton. This is bound to accentuate Sri Lanka's already severe pesticide problems.

Malaysia

As for most Third World countries, reliable statistics on pesticide poisoning in Malaysia are scanty, but Annual Reports of the Department of Chemistry give details of 422 cases between 1972 and 1976. The pesticides most often responsible were malathion (121 cases), paraquat (75 cases), methamidophos (31 cases) and dieldrin (26 cases). Others included endosulfan (24 cases) gamma BHC (23 cases) and DDT (21 cases).[48]

It is not clear whether these figures include intentional poisonings. Nevertheless, the potential for occupational and accidental poisoning in Malaysia is clearly illustrated by the lack of knowledge and precautions taken by farmers, as well as by the free availability of many potentially hazardous pesticides, which have been found on sale in most unsatisfactory conditions. Adulteration of chemicals has also been widespread. Recent legislation, if adequately enforced, will help to clear up some of these problems.

The Consumers' Association of Penang (CAP) and Sahabat Alam Malaysia (SAM — Friends of the Earth) have carried out a local survey of farmers' knowledge and practices. The survey concluded that farmers rarely followed prescribed instructions. "They have little knowledge," said SAM President, Encik Idris, "as to the toxicity, safe handling procedures and health hazards involved in using pesticides."[49] The survey also found that 43% of farmers who had used pesticides complained that they experienced some form of illness after applying the chemicals.[50]

CAP have also found pesticides on sale in shops, alongside food and even repacked into unlabelled bottles. In one case 2,4,5-T was purchased from a shop in Penang in an unlabelled sauce bottle which was actually kept on the same shelf as sauce and other food-stuffs.[51] A paper presented to a symposium in Portugal in 1975 said of Malaysia: "The manner of sale of pesticides leaves much to be desired because of their close association with food-stuffs in village shops".[52] The volume of pesticide use in Malaysia has been increasing dramatically in recent years. Imports more than doubled in volume between 1965 and 1975. In one rice growing area covering 260,000 acres, the use of pesticides per hundred tons of rice produced rose from 4.83 lbs in 1971 to 24.78 lbs by 1975. A study published in 1980 found high levels of organochlorine pesticides in the blood of padi (rice) farmers, and concluded that

> "Pesticide usage in the padi fields of Muda is becoming more and more excessive".

The study laid the blame partly on the treadmill effect which we have discussed in earlier chapters. Other reasons given for excessive use were aggressive marketing, over-eager extension workers and subsidies to farmers.[53]

Many pesticides which are banned or seriously restricted in the pesticide exporting countries were available in Malaysia in 1980. These included 2,4,5-T (banned in Sweden, restricted in the US, and the subject of controversy in Britain); heptachlor (banned in the EEC except for treatment of beet seed; being phased out for most uses in the US), and dieldrin (WHO: extremely hazardous; LD_{50}:10; banned in the EEC; cancelled for most uses in the US). Other pesticides classified by WHO as extremely hazardous, and available in Malaysia in 1980 were chlorfenvinphos (LD_{50}:10; covered by Health and Safety Regulations and Poisons Rules in UK) and phenylmercury acetate (LD_{50}:30; restricted in the EEC).[54]

At the same time, however, the Malaysian authorities have made efforts to control pesticide imports, sale and use by legislation. The Poisons Ordinance of 1952 banned some of the most hazardous products, including parathion and endrin. The Pesticides Act of 1974 will, when fully enforced, permit only registered pesticides to be sold in Malaysia. Other conditions include labelling and advertising regulations and specific measures to reduce the hazard of some chemicals. For example, isomalathion impurities in malathion and dioxin (TCDD) impurities in 2,4,5-T will be restricted in line with international regulations, while paraquat will be required to contain a stinking agent to prevent mistaken drinking. The implementation and enforcement of such legislation in the Third World presents great difficulties and, although passed in 1974, the Act is only beginning to be enforced in stages in the early 1980s, (labelling and advertising, for example, from January 1982). The Department of Agriculture claims that pesticides are no longer sold in improperly labelled containers and that education programmes for farmers are being carried out.[55] It was reported in July 1981, that the Ministry had received 1,912 applications to register pesticides under the 1974 Act. Of these, 600 were not registered and 319 were withdrawn by the applicants.[56]

Thailand

In Rajburi Province of Thailand between 1966 and 1970, there were 320 cases of pesticide poisoning, including 24 deaths.[57] In 1972, more than 450 cases of accidental poisoning were reported in Thailand, including about 40 deaths.[58]

Banpot Napompeth, Director of the National Biological Control Research Center in Thailand, says that all the problems of pesticide use

> "are accelerated through other social aspects of the farmers who,
> with relatively low literacy, are unaware of the danger of the
> pesticides and ignore safety precautions when handling pesticides.
> When affected from the misuse they usually ignore or are reluctant
> to seek medical treatment."[59]

Napompeth has described one of the horrifying practices which result from the availability of toxic pesticides under these conditions:

> "When mixing the formulation for spraying, the farmer may dip his
> finger into the mix and taste it by dabbing his finger to his tongue.
> If it gets numb it indicates the right concentration."[60]

The problems are enhanced by bad labelling and marketing practices, while even the government assistance programme has encouraged the use of pesticides whether there is real need or not.[61] Despite the regulations, labels often fail to include the name of the active ingredients, antidotes or first aid instructions.[62] Sales promotion encourages farmers in the belief that pesticides are the only way to deal with pests. This can make difficult the work of agencies engaged in the promotion of more integrated pest management strategies.[63]

A survey of pesticides found in farm holdings in Rajburi Province revealed the following among the most commonly used: methamidophos (207 holdings), methomyl (1965), ethyl parathion (94) and endrin (52). All of these are either unavailable in Britain or covered by Health and Safety Regulations. The survey report concludes:

> "Pesticides used in agricultural holdings are not necessarily those
> which are the best ones for the purpose sought by the farmer, but
> rather those which the retailers wish to push forward under the
> influence of the central distributors. Substantial divergences are
> found in... accuracy of labelling and warning against potential
> risk."[64]

Thailand has laws governing pesticides (the Poisonous Article Acts of 1967 and 1973), but enforcement has been ineffective or even "non-existent".[65] "Virtually no pesticides have been put under restricted use or banned in the country," says Napompeth.[66]

Indonesia

In Indonesia in 1967/8 a survey in Java and Sumatra collected information on 829 cases of pesticide poisoning, including 114 deaths[67] and in 1969 found 509 cases, with 125 deaths.[68] Pesticides responsible included both organochlorines and organophosphates. Pentachlorophenol, used as a weedkiller, defoliant and wood preservative, caused 30 poisonings in the sawmills of West Kalimantan in 1973.[69] Many of these cases apparently involved the use of empty pesticide containers for storage and transport of food and water. This is common in many parts of the Third World.

Jerry Adams, a volunteer funded by OXFAM working at an agricultural school in Indonesia, had the idea of purchasing a power-sprayer which could be hired out, with a trained operator, to local farmers. At the same time, the operator could teach the farmers about safe and proper use of pesticides. "At the moment," says Jerry, "the knowledge of spraying is terrible with very little, if any, understanding of the uses of various sprays".[70]

This view is supported by a survey carried out by an Indonesian consumer group (Yayasan Lembaga Konsumen) in West Java. They came to the following conclusions:

"Farmers had very poor knowledge on the use, storage and safety aspect of pesticides. The problem was heightened by the fact that too many brands circulated in the market... What's worse was that some brands were already prohibited for use by the Government. Safety measures like the use of gloves, masks, boots... were hardly known. Some farmers reportedly suffered health deficiencies like nausea, headaches, etc."[71]

The Philippines

In the Philippines, a study in one province revealed 38 deaths a year among young people aged 15-21 from pesticide poisoning.[72] A doctor who treats farmers in a clinic in Cotabato on the island of Mindanao reports that during peak spraying periods he treats 4 to 6 patients a day for pesticide poisoning.[73]

The Philippines, home of the International Rice Research Institute (IRRI) is the seat of the 'Green Revolution' in rice. The government-sponsored "Masagana 99" programme is directed at increasing rice production through the use of high-yielding varieties and inputs of fertilizers and pesticides. As a result, pesticide use among rice farmers is unusually widespread. Of 3-6 million hectares planted with rice in 1977, 95% were treated with pesticides.[74]

The rapid technological change in rice-growing in the Philippines appears to have outstripped the capability of those involved to understand the new techniques. This inevitably creates a pesticide-related health hazard. An anthropologist's survey in one area showed that farmers generally believed that any insect in a field is a pest to be liquidated. All farmers sprayed brown planthopper resistant varieties unnecessarily against brown planthopper. None of the farmers were aware that a leaky sprayer could kill them.[75] These farmers are not stupid, — and many are educated beyond primary level. But the sheer quantity of new ideas, concepts and information has been too rapid for them to develop their own understanding. Even the extension workers who are supposed to advise the farmers have in many instances been left behind.

In 1980 the Farmers Assistance Board (FAB) conducted a survey to examine farmers' ability to protect themselves from pesticide hazards:

"The interviews which FAB conducted in 1980 among 284 lowland and upland farmers showed that protective clothing are not within their financial reach. In addition, being uninformed about health hazards of pesticides, farmers are not conscious of the necessity of wearing protective clothing."[76]

The control of pesticides and their hazards in the Philippines is in the hands of the Fertilizer and Pesticide Authority (FPA), set up in 1977. The objectives of the FPA include the provision of assistance to farmers in increasing production and the supply of agricultural inputs, as well as the regulation of pesticides. It is also mandated:

"To educate the agricultural sector on the benefits as well as the hazards of pesticide use so it can utilize pesticides properly to promote human welfare while avoiding dangers to health and environmental pollution."[77]

The FPA has begun the training of 'agromedical' teams to cope with poisoning cases and has also started a certification scheme for pest control operators in an attempt to professionalise the occupation. The FPA is also responsible for monitoring pesticide residues in food and the environment.

The import and use of certain chemicals has been restricted by the FPA: as of October 1980, for example, ethyl parathion, 2,4,5-T, leptophos and DBCP were banned except for emergencies; DDT was allowed only for malaria control, and aldrin, dieldrin, chlordane and heptachlor restricted to soil treatment only (not for direct application to crops). Because of the hazard to applicators, methamidophos, dichlorvos and mevinphos were not permitted for use in rice. Aldicarb and paraquat were classified as "too hazardous for general use".[78] To date it seems that these regulations have not been effective. The FAB says:

"FPA... has not been effective in exercising to the fullest its police powers. It banned/restricted pesticides... but most of these are still sold to farmers through local dealers."[79]

The price list of insecticides recommended for the Masagana 99 programme in 1980 included azinphos ethyl (WHO: highly hazardous; LD_{50}:12; UK: covered by Health and Safety Regulations (H & S)); phosphamidon (WHO: extremely hazardous; LD_{50}:17; UK: H & S and Poisons Rules), and monocrotophos (WHO: highly hazardous; LD_{50}:14).[80]

Once again, many pesticides are available to farmers which are widely restricted around the world. They are supplied by a number of European and American companies, as well as some from India, Japan and other countries. The farmers are largely unaware of the hazards and of the necessary protective measures. Also they cannot afford the equipment necessary for the safe use of the chemicals recommended to them.

India

A survey of farm workers engaged in spraying in Gujarat showed that they were not provided with face masks, only 50% covered their nose and mouth with a cloth, 20% failed to wash after spraying.[81] Mr. S. Selliah, Asian representative of the International Federation of Agricultural and Allied Workers, said:

"A number of people get affected by occupational pesticide poisoning but people don't usually report to the hospital until it's too late. Also, the sufferer is usually also suffering from other health problems which contribute to death. This means that one of the other causes will usually be recorded as the cause of death... Pesticides are often mixed by hand and sometimes pesticide powders are just sprinkled by hand onto the crops."[82]

OXFAM's Assistant Field Director for East India, Lincoln Young reports that highly toxic pesticides like Metasystox and parathion are applied without protective clothing. These and other pesticides restricted in the West may be cheap but are also extremely hazardous in a country where the conditions necessary for safe use do not exist.

Even for organised plantation workers it is a struggle to obtain even the simplest protective clothing. Mr R.M.R. Singham of the General Employees Union, representing 10,000 workers in the Indian State of Karnataka, says:

"In Karnataka Plantations the workers who are using the pesticides do not get any protective clothing. This Union has raised a demand with Karnataka Planters' Association for gloves and face-masks."[83]

Pesticides mentioned by Singham include disulfoton, phosphamidon and endosulfan, all of which are covered by Health and Safety regulations in Britain requiring the use of protective clothing. In 1980 a team from the National Institute of Occupational Health had recently spent two months investigating conditions on tea plantations in South India. They found that there is an unnecessary risk to workers' health from pesticides. On one plantation 40 different chemicals were used. Although pesticide applicators were given some protective clothing, their assistants were unprotected even though they mixed the pesticides — the most hazardous part of the operation. The study is not yet complete but workers in a sample had reduced levels of cholinesterase (an effect of certain pesticides) and workers complained of headaches and insomnia.[84]

Dr. Y.R. Reddy, superintendant and paediatrician at the Niloufar Children's Hospital in Hyderabad describes the conditions under which pesticides are often stored and used in India:

"Poor people live in one room only," he says, "so they keep their pesticides in the room as well. They live there, cook there and eat there. The powder is in the air. When they spray their crops, the spray sometimes drifts into the house, and children are exposed."[85]

Pakistan

Pakistan was the site in 1976 of a massive poisoning outbreak among spraymen in the malaria control programme. More than a third of the programme's 7,500 field workers were affected and five people died.[86] The chemical in use was malathion, usually considered relatively safe. This tragic episode was the result of a combination of poor work practices, including mixing the pesticide by hand, and the presence of isomalathion impurities in malathion supplied by two Italian companies, Rumianca and Snia Viscosa.[87]

The report of a study team which visited Pakistan two years earlier[88], lists a number of poisoning cases, details poor working practices resulting from a lack of understanding of the dangers of pesticide use, and describes the inability of medical services to cope with poisoning cases. The potential for the later disaster was apparent, yet appears not to have been taken sufficiently seriously by either the Pakistani authorities or the companies supplying pesticides.

* * * * * * *

We have seen how, in many Third World countries, pesticide poisoning is not an uncommon occurrence. We have also seen some of the reasons: the free availability of dangerous chemicals under conditions hostile to their safe and effective use. In some places these conditions are compounded by the effects of the pesticide treadmill, the promotional efforts of pesticide salesmen, inadequate labelling and the inability of governments properly to enforce pesticide control legislation.

Much of the remedy lies in the hands of Third World governments who could help by improving their agricultural extension services, their legislation and its enforcement. It is evident, though, that they face great financial and administrative difficulties in carrying out these measures. International organisations and aid programmes can and do assist by providing technical expertise and training programmes. Companies have achieved much in devising safer formulations of hazardous pesticides and hopeful progress has been made in the development of application equipment with safety advantages.

Nevertheless, much more should be done. Companies should begin by including maximum safety information in advertisements and labels in local languages. International organisations could help by drawing up and monitoring codes of practice for advertising and labelling. The governments of pesticide exporting countries could complement the legislation of hard-pressed Third World governments by ensuring that no hazardous pesticide is exported without full information on its toxicity, regulatory status and safety precautions being sent to, and acknowledged by, the importers and their governments. Ultimately the governments of exporting countries could take the power to prevent the export of dangerous pesticides, particularly those banned or heavily restricted in their countries of origin, unless they were completely satisfied after consultation with the recipient country government that these products were of the type and quality required, taking account of conditions of use and the alternatives available.[89]

To the extent that poisoning is a side-effect of the pesticide treadmill, a significant part of the solution must lie in the promotion of more sensible agricultural pest management strategies. This means reducing reliance on chemicals for pest control by promoting and encouraging integrated pest management. In the long-term this is the most important step which must be taken. It must begin immediately and urgently and far greater resources be devoted to it than at present. This will be discussed in detail in Chapter 10.

Finally, Third World countries should continue to develop effective systems of rural primary health care, and these systems should incorporate the means to prevent and treat pesticide poisoning. This implies a far greater co-operation between health and agricultural services in what has been termed an 'agro-medical' approach to pesticide management.[90]

Residues
in Food

RESIDUES IN FOOD

"Market women travel to district market towns where they sell the insecticides to local farmers and fishermen, and in turn buy their fish for exportation to larger market areas. The fishermen or farmers then use the insecticides by pouring them into the water of small shallow streams, following the flow downstream until the fish begin floating to the surface where they are collected for salting and smoking... Everyone agrees that fishing with poison is bad. Most don't realise how bad... The same fishermen who use the method complain that they are now in a vicious circle: they cannot catch enough using nets and hooks to pay for or maintain the very costly nets and fishing gear. Actually, poison represents the cheapest, easiest, most convenient and therefore most profitable method of fishing available... The fish population is dropping by about 20% per year... People in fishing villages complain of blurred vision, dizziness and vomiting, but none makes the connection between these symptoms and the poison."[1]

Fishing by pesticides is a common practice in Ghana, the African country which is the source of this story. It is one extreme example of the ability of pesticides to be stored in food and to cause poisoning symptoms when the food is later consumed.

There are four ways in which pesticides residues can get into the food people eat. Firstly, residues can enter food as a result of an illegitimate use of the pesticides. This is the case in the example above, where a chemical is used to catch fish -- obviously not a recommended use. Secondly, food can become contaminated with pesticides during transport or storage. Problems can also occur when seed treated with a pesticide is used as food rather than being planted. Thirdly, residues can arise as a result of the legitimate use of pesticides to protect crops. If these pesticides are used excessively, ill-advisedly or at a date too near to the harvest, then the residues may be above accepted limits and possibly hazardous to health. Finally, people may ingest pesticides in food which is gathered from a pesticide-laden environment such as fish from rice fields. This latter will be discussed in the next chapter.

The contamination of wheat with parathion led to about 100 deaths in the South Indian State of Kerala in 1958. More recently 250 villagers were poisoned in Uttar Pradesh in North India due to wheat contamination with BHC during storage.[2]

Pesticide tins are used to serve local beer in the market in Awassa, Ethiopia.

55

The use of treated seed for food led to one of the worst epidemics of pesticide poisoning. This occurred in Iraq in 1971/2. [3] Wheat and barley seed was imported which had been treated with a methyl mercury fungicide. Warnings issued to farmers not to eat the grain were insufficient or went unheeded. Warnings on some sacks appeared in English and Spanish only and, in some cases, the seed arrived too late for planting. Many farmers' families ate the treated grain or fed it to their animals. Official Iraqi figures say that 6,530 people were poisoned and 459 died. Many of the survivors were permanently affected by the crippling effects or mercury poisoning. Journalist Edward Hughes visited Iraq in 1973. His investigations and discussions with experts led him to estimate the true scale of the catastrophe at 100,000 injured and 6,000 dead.

Pesticides applied to food crops in the field can also leave potentially harmful residues. Organochlorine pesticides in particular can persist in foodstuffs for a considerable period. If crops are sprayed immediately prior to harvest without an appropriate waiting period, even organophosphate residues can persist until the food is in the hands of the consumer.

Many countries set maximum permissible levels of particular pesticide residues in food with the intention of protecting the health of consumers. In addition, international standards are established jointly by FAO and WHO through the Codex Alimentarius Commission. The international recommendations are particularly useful to Third World countries whose expertise and resources would be overstretched if they had to draw up, monitor and enforce their own local standards. The Codex residue limits also provide an international standard which can be applied to foodstuffs traded in the world market. The Codex maximum residue limits are set after joint meetings of WHO and FAO expert committees and consultation with governments. The limits are based on a determination of residues which would result from 'good agricultural practice', but must also be consistent with the 'Maximum Acceptable Daily Intake' (ADI) of a chemical determined on toxicological grounds. 'Good agricultural practice' is defined as:

"The officially recommended or authorised usage of pesticides under practical conditions at any stage of production, storage, transport, distribution and processing of food and other agricultural commodities, bearing in mind the variations in requirements between regions and taking into account the minimum quantities necessary to achieve adequate control, the pesticides being applied in such a manner as to leave residues that are the smallest amounts practicable and that are toxicologically acceptable."

In other words, the limit should be low enough to protect the consumer and high enough to protect the crops. A residue in excess of Codex limits indicates two things: firstly that pesticides have been improperly used in the production, processing or storage of that product, and secondly that there is a potential threat to the health of the consumer. This latter threat is likely to be fairly small if the Codex level is only just exceeded since the ADI is ''that daily intake which during an entire lifetime appears to be without appreciable risk on the basis of all the known facts at the time''.[4]

This safety margin is desirable since new facts may come to light in the future, and since a particular residue will, in reality, be consumed alongside many other residues in the total diet. The safety margin is also perfectly feasible since crops can be adequately protected, through good agricultural practice, without exceeding it. Residues above Codex limits should not occur. If they do, action should be taken to improve agricultural practice.

It is sometimes thought that residues are completely destroyed if food is properly washed and cooked. This is not always so. Pesticide residues in food may be reduced by washing and cooking but even boiling may remove only 35-60% of organophosphate residues and 20-25% of organochlorines. Residues above tolerance limits do occur in cooked food.[5]

Excessive residues in food can be prevented by restricting the use of the more persistent pesticides (those which degrade slowly are stored in foodstuffs and in the body's tissues) and by adhering to proper waiting periods between the last pesticide application and the harvest of the crop. These waiting periods themselves also depend on the relative persistence of the pesticide concerned.

Appropriate periods are not always adhered to, especially in the Third World, because farmers are anxious to protect their crops right up to the day of harvest. Pest-free and undamaged produce may fetch a higher price in the market than even slightly damaged produce which is of equal value in terms of taste and nutrition.

Food products of Third World countries may be sold either in local markets or for export to other countries. The presence of residues in each case gives rise to different problems and the two cases will therefore be treated in turn. The residue legislation of some Third World countries and its enforcement will also be examined.

Local Markets

The first problem, then, is that of residues in food in local markets. Since such food is likely to be consumed at a shorter interval after harvest, the potential for excess residues is greater and concerns even residues of pesticides having relatively short persistence. Also, these less persistent pesticides include some of those which are most toxic.

In India permissible residue limits have been set under the Prevention of Food Adulteration Act, 1954 (PFA Rules). Unfortunately enforcement of these limits is virtually nonexistent and significant proportions of food marketed in India appear, from the few studies carried out, to contain residues beyond the permissible limits.[6]

One seven-year study, for example, took over 1,000 samples of foodstuffs from Hyderabad market. More than 35% were found to contain organochlorine residues exceeding tolerance limits.[7] In another study most of the milk marketed in the Punjab was found to contain DDT residues above maximum limits[8], and all 300 samples of leafy vegetables analysed in Mysore contained excessive residues of BHC.[9] Entomologists from the Indian Agricultural Research Institute have drawn up a list of 27 insecticide applications on 9 crops which "may be reckoned as hazardous and should be discontinued". Their conclusion was that,

> "Taking into consideration our capacity and facilities available, the Central Insecticides Board should review its policies and restrict the number of insecticides to a minimum possible. This would enable the government to enforce legal provisions and safeguard the health of consumers."[10]

The residues in foodstuffs identified in these studies can accumulate in the bodies of consumers and indeed, as early as 1965, it was reported that Indians carried the highest load of DDT in their bodies. Indians may ingest 20-40 times as much DDT as Britons.[11] The 1965 study found concentrations of 20 parts per million in the fat of Indians in the Delhi area, and this was confirmed by another study 10 years later. A more recent study in the Punjab found lower levels, showing that there are regional variations. Food is reckoned to be the main source of this contamination.[12]

Despite such apparently high residues it is not clear to what degree these represent a hazard to health even in the longer term. Also, DDT has a relatively low acute toxicity and so is less hazardous in use than many of the pesticides which might replace it. For these reasons Third World countries may hesitate to ban its use in agriculture. On the other hand, the ability of DDT to accumulate in the environment and in people's bodies has caused it to be widely banned in the rich world. These same characteristics should compel Third World countries to use it as little and as cautiously as possible.

An analysis of horticultural crops in Kenya indicated that 40% of samples contained residues above recommended levels. Excessively high residues were also found on cotton-seed cake used for livestock feed despite the fact that the pesticides concerned, aldrin and dieldrin, are not recommended for use on cotton in Kenya. It may be that this feed was imported from neighbouring Uganda.[13] Aldrin and dieldrin are persistent organochlorines, banned or severely restricted in Europe and the US.

In Sri Lanka analysis of vegetable samples showed, in 1978, widespread presence of pesticide residues, although these were generally well below Codex tolerance levels. Rice samples from some districts, though, were found to contain residues of dieldrin and heptachlor much higher than Codex limits. Also, analysis of fat tissues of patients in Kandy showed DDT residues ranging from 10 to 102 parts per million, very high relative to world averages of 5 to 10 ppm.[14]

These studies carried out in Sri Lanka refer only to organochlorine pesticides, but organophosphates could be a problem too, despite their relatively short persistence. Even with the least persistent pesticides at least three or four days waiting time should be left between last application and harvest. Sri Lanka's agricultural research institute would prefer a general waiting time of 2 or 3 weeks.[15] Yet in Sri Lanka, as in India, it is fairly common, according to extension workers, for vegetable crops to be sprayed only one day before going to market.[16]

Any ineffective or excessive use of pesticides can only add to the potential danger from the accumulation of residues in food and in people. It would help to reduce this danger if pesticide users were given better information about pest management and specifically about the necessary waiting periods to prevent excessive residues. Residue problems and waiting periods are rarely mentioned in advertisements and even in information leaflets and labels are often hidden in small print or left out altogether. Entomologists R.L. Kalra and R.P. Chawla from the Punjab Agricultural University sum up the problems with reference to India:

"The failure in regulating pesticide residues in India, arises from a lack of appreciation that pesticides are products of technological society... As pesticides are costly inputs, the farmer is not likely to use them in quantities more than the required, provided the information on the minimum effective dosage of a pesticide for pest control is made available to him. The mechanism for providing this information to the user has not so far been developed in the country. Under the circumstances it will be unrealistic to expect any control on pesticide residue. The PFA rules presently look like putting the cart before the horse."[17]

Thus, while residue legislation has a role, the first priority should be to provide the conditions under which 'good agricultural practice' can become a real possibility. This means improving extension and advisory services as well as labelling and advertising.

The difficulty of providing the correct information to the farmer is accentuated by the lack of information, in some Third World countries, even on the part of the regulatory authorities. Dr. Frank A. Del Prado is head of the Plant Protection and Production Division of Surinam's Ministry of Agriculture. Speaking to a US conference in 1979 he described some of the problems:

"No data on waiting periods are available to us. Frequently we cannot advise a farmer on how many days he will have to wait before harvesting his crops after spraying. Some information is available for crops and pesticides in temperate climates, but for the tropics there is no written material, and information cannot be obtained from manufacturers... We lack not only laboratory equipment but also trained personnel... As you see it is a complex problem, and there is no easy solution. But something has to be done, and fast. It is a common practice among farmers in many countries to spray the insects they see on their crops and then sell the produce the next day on the market."[18]

Exports

The problems of Third World countries in effectively controlling residues can have consequences beyond the relatively little demonstrated long-term health effects of domestic consumption. Many people in the Third World depend for their livelihoods on the export of agricultural produce to the rich world. For the foreseeable future such dependence exists, even though many Third World countries are taking measures to reduce it. These important export markets can be endangered by the presence in exported foodstuffs of excessive pesticide residues.

In many countries of the rich world, such as the US, Japan and Canada, maximum residue limits have statutory authority and imported foods are monitored for residues.[19] Although much imported food containing residues still gets through to the rich world consumer, in some cases it is turned away -- at considerable cost to the exporters in the Third World.

In the UK it is not clear to what degree excessive residues are being imported in food. Surveys of residues are carried out by the Working Party on Pesticide Residues and studies have been made to determine the level of residues in the total diet of an average Briton. Systematic monitoring is carried out of residues in human body fat and also surveys are conducted by the Association of Public Analysts. All these studies indicate that, in general, the levels of pesticide residues in the British diet are not excessive. None of these assessments, though, refers specifically to *imported* foodstuffs, although some of these may be included.[20]

Although there are no statutory limits to residues in food in the UK, the quality of food on sale is governed by two relevant laws. The Food and Drugs Act, 1955, provides that food should be fit for human consumption and should not be injurious to health. The Imported Food Regulations, 1968, make it an offence to import food which is unfit for human consumption. These regulations are enforced by the Port Health Authorities who would "have regard to the Codex residue limits as presumptive standards".[21] Analysis of imported food under these regulations for pesticide residues is, however, not carried out on a regular or routine basis. In fact there is very little information available in the UK which could help us to gauge how far agricultural products imported from the Third World contain residues in excess of Codex limits.

In the US, where regular monitoring is carried out, the position is clearer. The Food and Drug Administration conducted spot checks of about 1% of shipments of imported raw agricultural commodities between 1977 and 1979. Of the shipments tested 5% were found to contain residues for which no US tolerance levels exist.[22] These include pesticides which are not permitted for use within the US. Out of 1,258 samples of produce from Mexico in 1977, 7.2% were found to contain residue levels above the tolerance of the US Environmental Protection Agency (EPA), or residues of pesticides not permitted in the US. Forty shipments were denied entry as a result.[23]

As well as representing a cost to the exporting country, the existence of residues in internationally traded agricultural produce must represent some level of risk, albeit a small one, to the consumers of the importing country. In 1976 some workers in a florist shop in Colorado suffered poisoning symptoms after handling cut flowers contaminated with demeton, an extremely hazardous organophosphate. Flowers are not subject to residue tolerance in the US and high residues have been found on flowers imported from Latin America.[24]

Incidents such as this do *not* demonstrate a conflict between the rich countries, which want to protect their consumers from residues, and the poor countries, which want to export as much agricultural produce as possible. Rather, they demonstrate a joint interest between the rich countries and the Third World. It is in the interest of both that pesticide use in the Third World should be properly regulated and controlled, and pest management techniques which minimise pesticide use should be encouraged. In this way consumers and workers in both countries would be protected and Third World countries' products would not be barred from rich world markets. This mutuality of interest between the peoples of rich and poor countries should be reflected in the policies of their governments and the practices of their companies. Some US trades unionists put it like this:

"There needs to be a clear understanding that our stewardship of
the pesticides technologies extends to the protection — when
possible — of everyone affected in any country. It is our technology.
In addition to this ethical reason, there is the practical fact that
adequate protection of users in other countries means protection
for our people simply because the technology would be controlled,
ie properly used. Proper use means a reduction in residual pesticide
through integrated pest management."[25]

Thus, the costs to Third World countries of having their exports rejected, is a cost of the uncontrolled trade in, and use of pesticides. These costs are to be taken seriously. In Pakistan, for example, a 1974 study team reported that:

"Agricultural crops . . . are the chief export commodity of Pakistan. Many consuming nations have established monitoring systems for pesticide residues on agricultural products. The potential economic loss to Pakistan is great if quality control is not assured at this end. We have heard of one shipment of tobacco which was refused by the receiving country on the basis of unacceptable organochlorine residue."[26]

In Central America cattle are exposed to pesticides by eating forage contamined by spray drift from the cotton fields and animal feeds containing cotton-seed meal contaminated by pesticides. This coexistence of cattle and cotton has led to high residues in meat and milk. The ICAITI report found DDT residues in milk in Guatemala 90 times higher than the US limit of 0.05 ppm. Beef exports began to be rejected by importers in the early 1970s, since when some residue analysis has been carried out by meat packers prior to shipment.[27]

US inspectors can reject beef with DDT residues in the fat above 5 ppm. The average in beef samples from cotton areas of Guatemala between 1973 and 1976 was 5.76 ppm. In Guatemala and El Salvador between 1973 and 1976 12.6% of samples analysed were above US tolerance limits. "Over the last 15 years ," says the ICAITI report, "the beef industry in the four countries [Guatemala, El Salvador, Nicaragua and Honduras] has had increased costs of over $1.7 million [nearly £1 million] because of pesticide contamination."[28]

Banpot Napompeth, Director of the National Biological Control Research Center, has described the problem as it affects Thailand. Thai pesticide legislation does not, he says,

"provide adequate regulations to prevent the contamination of farm products. . . Contamination of agricultural exports from Thailand could lead to the ruin of the economy of the nation, for Thailand depends heavily on its exports, such as rice, sorghum and others. At one time tobacco leaves from Thailand were rejected by Germany on the basis of pesticide contamination above the tolerance level."[29]

The rejection of exports, then, can combine with the cost of analysing for residues to produce a considerable economic loss. Also, the commodity which is declared unfit for export may end up on the domestic market contributing to pesticide accumulation in the people of the Third World countries themselves.

* * * * * * *

The residue problem in local markets or in export crops will not be solved by legislation against residues alone. More importantly, it must be solved by improving pest control practices. This means improving the standard of information given to farmers. As long as pesticides continue to be promoted as safe and profitable panaceas; as long as warnings are given only in the small print or not at all; as long as labels appear without instructions in local languages, and as long as spraying by calendar is accepted and integrated pest management deferred until tomorrow, the residue problem will remain, as will all the other problems of inappropriate, uncontrolled and excessive pesticide use.

61

Nevertheless, better pest management practices *may* result from the realisation of a residue problem. Many Third World countries lack the facilities to monitor residues and only become aware of a problem when they are informed by a country which imports from them and which monitors those imports for residues.

Concern about residues and consequent economic losses has encouraged some Third World countries to adopt better pest management practices and to regulate pesticide more effectively. In Sri Lanka, for example, the Tea Research Institute has developed an integrated pest management programme which appears to be achieving good results by maximising the controlling effect of natural enemies, and by minimising pesticide use and making it more selective.[30]

Third World countries are faced with difficult choices. Excess residues threaten their people's health and their valuable export markets, but they are often unable to enforce sophisticated residue legislation. One option left to them is to ban the agricultural use of some of the persistent organochlorines even where these could still have some acceptable uses if properly restricted.

A complete ban may be the best choice and it has been made by some countries. In Sri Lanka DDT was banned largely in order to protect tea exports.[31] Uraguay and Bolivia have also banned some organochlorines for similar reasons.[32] These choices are difficult and can only be made by Third World countries themselves. There are, though, specific measures which can be taken by the countries which export pesticides to the Third World and import Third World agricultural commodities. These measures would help Third World governments to control the import and use of pesticides and would help to protect consumers in rich and in poor countries.

The rich countries should routinely monitor residues in imported foodstuffs. The information gained would give a reliable and objective measure of the problem, which would indicate the scale of pesticide misuse in the food exporting country. This information would also enable the Third World country to gauge the severity of the threat to its export markets and so devise a suitable response. If the information were issued on a regular basis, the Third World country would be able to act before its exports were actually being turned away.

The rich countries which impose tolerance limits on imports, or which are concerned about residues in imported food, also have a responsibility to control their exports of pesticides. This entails ensuring, as the US has begun to do, that no pesticide may be exported without complete and appropriate information reaching importers and the governments of importing countries. The need for information also includes locally applicable waiting periods determined for particular pesticides.

Third World countries could be given assistance to set up residue analysis facilities, perhaps on a regional basis to begin with. They could also be helped to develop effective domestic regulations. FAO already gives some assistance of this kind.

The real solution to the residue problems, as with all the other pesticide-related problems discussed in this book, is to ensure that as far as possible pest management practices in the Third World are safe and effective, and based on an integration of techniques which avoids the most toxic and the most persistent chemicals as far as possible.

6 Pesticides and the Third World Environment

PESTICIDES AND THE THIRD WORLD ENVIRONMENT

In 1975, health authorities in the Malnad area of Karnataka in South India began to report a mysterious new disease. It emerged that the first cases had begun to appear in 1969/70, and by 1977 over 200 people were affected in 40 villages. For the victims it began with intermittent pain in the hip and knee joints which later became continuous until some could hardly stand up. This crippling deformity, later given the rather long-winded name of 'Endemic Familial Arthritis of Malnad' (EFAM), appears to be linked to pesticide use.[1]

The people affected by EFAM were all poor people of low caste. At certain times of year, especially when food is short, the poorer villagers eat crabs which are found in the rice fields. At the time the disease appeared there had been two important changes in the area. Firstly, the landowners had stopped serving food to the labourers as part of their wages and secondly the Green Revolution had brought high-yielding seed varieties and pesticides to the area. So, not only were the poor thrown into greater reliance on the paddy-field crabs for food, but also those same paddy–fields were increasingly contaminated with pesticides, including parathion and endrin. Due to inbreeding and special genetic characteristics, the people of Malnad were particularly susceptible to the apparent effects of pesticide residues in the environment, consumed via the paddy-field crabs.

This story may be exceptional in terms of the impact of pesticides on people's health but it illustrates perfectly the close relationship between Third World people and their environment. This relationship is absolutely crucial to the poor, especially those who subsist on marginal diets. In Malnad, as in many other parts of Asia, fish and other aquatic organisms have died as a result of pesticide applications. In the rich world action has been taken to prevent damage to the environment caused by pesticides, but while the death of fish in a rich world river may mean little more than the loss of a day's pleasure for an angler, for the Third World's poor it can be literally a matter of life and death.

Something like 305 million kgs (675 million lbs.) weight of pesticides enter the Third World environment every year. Insofar as these pesticides are applied excessively or in a wasteful manner, they accentuate environmental problems unnecessarily. Aerial spraying, for example is especially wasteful because as little as 25-50% of the pesticide actually lands in the crop area.[2]

Asia's rice farmers really are a part of their environment. In 1972 the UC/AID Pest Management Programme sent a questionnaire to 54 organisations or individuals in a number of different countries. One of the respondents described the situation:

"In many ways, the rice farmers really live in the rice field environment. Their houses are surrounded by rice fields, they work barefooted in the fields, wash in the water spilling from the fields, their cattle drink it and their fowls peck in and around paddy-fields...

There is no doubt that indiscriminate use of pesticides has an impact on the environment. These are reports of fish kills, particularly in the rice fields and irrigation canals, and there have been fatal cases of livestock poisoning (grazing on contaminated pastures) in plantations."[3]

The effects of pesticides on fish, especially in Asia, are of crucial importance to the people for whom fish represent an important source of protein. In Indonesia, for example, fish farming in rice fields produces about a quarter of all fresh, closed-water fish output[4] and fish constitutes two-thirds of the animal protein consumed. In 1969 fish were harvested from 3 million hectares of rice fields in Indonesia with a potential annual production of 600,000 tonnes.[5] The Threshold International Center for Environmental Renewal, commenting on the US Agency for International Development's environmental impact statement on its pesticide programme, concluded that:

"The consequences to Asian farmers of the use of chlorinated hydrocarbons in the control of the rice stem borer are the elimination of fish from rice paddies."[6]

Robert Richter

Aerial spraying, which uses more pesticide than necessary, is only feasible on a large scale. Farm workers and the rural poor are exposed to it and suffer from its effects on the environment.

64

In some parts of South-east Asia, as a result of the effect of religious beliefs on diet, fish is the *only* source of animal protein.[7] Paddy-field fish cultivation also represents a way of diversifying farmers' activities and increasing their food self-reliance. The substitution of Green Revolution rice monocropping, with high pesticide inputs and lower depths of water, adversely affects fish output and increases farmers' reliance on cash-cropping. This may or may not yield income sufficient to replace the nutritional losses resulting from reduced fish production.[8]

Although other agricultural changes, such as double cropping, have adversely affected paddy-field fish populations, there is no doubt that pesticides have played an important part. In Malaysia for example "pesticide poisoning is certainly directly responsible for decrease in fish yield".[9] It also has more indirect effects on the paddy-field ecosystem. Sub-lethal doses can affect the structure of the aquatic community, the food chain and the behaviour patterns of fish. The result is that both persistent pesticides and regular applications of less persistent ones can adversely affect the fish population.

Paddy-field fish stocks may include more than one species and in one study all pesticides tested were toxic to one species or another.[10] Even very low doses of some pesticides can affect the fish population by reducing enzyme levels and so increasing their susceptibility to other stresses.[11] Pesticides found to be lethal to fish in Malaysian paddy-fields in a number of studies include endosulfan, endrin, dieldrin and azinphos-ethyl.[12] So, in Malaysia over the last ten years the paddy-field fish harvest has decreased. The rice farmers are losing an important supplementary income and a cheap source of valuable protein.

And it is not just in Malaysia. From the Philippines, for example, comes this report:

"Previously, the farmer easily provided for his meals by catching fish in the rice field, the last routine in his early morning work in the farm before coming home for breakfast. But not any more. Fish in the rice fields are disappearing. So are snails, oysters, crabs, shrimps, frogs and other aquatic creatures."[13]

In Bangladesh some fish kills have been reported despite government testing of pesticides for fish toxicity. The rice fields are connected to the nation's water-ways and so there is some risk to river, pond and paddy fish which form an important part of the diet of many Bangladeshis.[14] In Central America the evidence suggests reductions in fish populations as a result of heavy pesticide use in the cotton fields.[15] There, as in Asia, fish are an important protein source.

In Zimbabwe during 1981 there was considerable public debate concerning the impact of pesticides, especially DDT, on the environment. W.R. Thompson, a Provincial Warden for the Department of National Parks and Wild Life Management, has expressed particular concern. Some predatory birds, he says, are threatened with extinction and the evidence

"points to the fact that our rivers are seriously polluted and that there is a genuine threat to our fish populations which has not yet been taken seriously by our agricultural scientists. Our fishing industry provides about 15,000 tonnes of protein per year."[16]

As has been seen in the last chapter, the environmental impact of DDT in particular presents Third World countries with a difficult dilemma. Alternative pesticides which are less persistent also tend to be more expensive and more toxic. By banning DDT, Third World countries could be replacing environmental problems with those of occupational and accidental poisoning. On the other hand DDT is a broad-spectrum chemical which has been in use for many years and therefore problems of resistance and natural enemy mortality may be added to the environmental consequences. Also, where DDT is used in vector control, the cessation of its use in agriculture could help to prolong its usefulness in the fight against disease.

As well as fish, there are some reports of the death of domestic animals as a result of pesticide use. This can also be a severe blow to poor rural families. The death of 1,300 water buffalo in Egypt associated with the use of the pesticide letophos, for example, was described earlier.[17] In Bangladesh, the OXFAM-funded project SCONE (Society for Conservation of Nature and Environment) reported in September 1981 that

> "pesticides used on croplands in Barisal in the South seeped to the water-logged bog area and hundreds of head of cattle drinking water from the polluted bog had died".[18]

Some pesticides, including chlordane, endrin and heptachlor, all still available in some Third World countries, are also highly toxic to earthworms which play an important role in circulating and aerating the soil.[19] Bees, too, are affected. They play an essential role in pollinating crop plants, as well as being kept for honey production. In some cotton growing areas of Tanzania and Kenya, bee-keeping is non-existent largely as a result of insecticides.[20] The huge potential cost of the loss of bees is indicated by studies in the US. They have estimated costs as follows:

> "For our analysis of the environmental costs, we assumed the minimum estimate that the pollination losses due to pesticides are at least $80 million [£34 million]. Adding the cost of reduced pollination to the other environmental costs of pesticides on honey bees and wild bees, the total annual loss is calculated to be about $135 million [£58 million]."[21]

At present levels of use, the impact of pesticides on the Third World environment appears to be relatively small. But pesticide use is increasing and there are some areas where environmental effects are already appearing. The closeness of the poor to the agricultural environment makes this a problem which must be taken very seriously and dealt with before it goes any further. For rural Third World people, concern for the environment is not just a matter of 'amenity' or the enjoyment of a day out in the country. Rather, the environmental impact of pesticides can have a dramatic effect on their livelihoods, most particularly through the impact on the supply of fish and other marine life which provide food.

* * * * * * *

The environmental problems discussed in this chapter demonstrate the need for effective controls especially on the availability and use of the persistent organochlorine pesticides. Although some of these present relatively little occupational hazard they do present a threat to the environment and there is still a need for restrictions on their use. Since many of these chemicals are banned or severely restricted in the pesticide exporting countries, there is a special responsibility when they are sold to Third World countries. This mutual responsibility was summed up in a 1977 resolution of the governing council of UNEP. This urged

"governments to take steps to ensure that potentially harmful chemicals, in whatever form or commodity, which are unacceptable for domestic purposes in the exporting country, are not permitted to be exported without the knowledge and consent of appropriate authorities in the importing country".[22]

In addition, and in the long term of the greatest importance, less damaging alternative methods of pest management should be encouraged and should replace reliance on pesticides wherever possible, although of course the environmental impact of cultural, biological and other forms of pest management also needs to be analysed and borne in mind in devising policies.

In the words of a 1972 UC/AID International Survey on pesticide use:

"The dangers of environmental contamination require a rigorous re-examination of chemical pest control methods currently in vogue in the LDCs."[23]

Weighing the Costs and Benefits

WEIGHING THE COSTS AND BENEFITS

"The effect of not spraying tropical crops would of course be disastrous, and the resulting famine would be the greatest disaster the world has ever known,"

says Dr. D.G. Hessayon of The British Agrochemicals Association.[1]

Similar views are often expressed by representatives of the pesticides industry and it is essential that any serious discussion of pesticide use in the Third World should include analysis of these issues. There are two questions which should be asked. Firstly, how do the costs and benefits of pesticide use really balance out? Secondly, are those costs and benefits distributed in such a way that their removal would seriously worsen the livelihood and food supply of the poorest people? This chapter will look at the first of these questions and the next chapter at the second.

In both chapters, we will consider the costs and benefits of the use of pesticides in *agriculture*, although the benefits of pesticides used in the control of malaria and other vector-borne diseases should not be forgotten. The loss of benefit through resistance among malaria-carrying mosquitoes has been described in Chapter 3. Insofar as this constitutes a 'cost' of *agricultural* pesticide use in the Third World, it will be included in this discussion.

Any attempt to weigh the costs and benefits must begin with a discussion of the theoretical results of a complete abandonment of pesticides since this is Dr. Hessayon's hypothesis, even though there is no serious support (least of all from OXFAM) for such a policy. If it is accepted that some pesticide use is desirable, then decisions must be made about which particular pesticides are made available to farmers and with what safeguards and controls. The farmer, finally, must choose the pattern of pesticide use most suited to his or her individual needs and circumstances. Decisions at all these levels require consideration of the relative costs and benefits of particular courses of action. In examining these questions, therefore, it is also necessary to look at the value and limitations of the technique of cost-benefit analysis.

Perhaps the major difficulty in weighing costs and benefits is the impossibility of putting a value on human lives and suffering. If this is attempted it can create paradoxical results. For example, if illness is measured by the cost of treatment, then the illness which is treated will be given greater weight than that which is not treated even though the latter is likely to bring greater suffering. Other problems arise from the necessity to compare costs and benefits in the present with those in the future which also have different likelihoods of occurring.

How, for example, do we balance tomorrow's possible disaster against today's certain benefit? How do we reconcile the values attached by different people to different events? For example, the poisoning of a farm labourer will be given a higher value by the labourer and his family than by his employer or by a politician in the capital city. And what should be done if scientists and doctors are uncertain, for example, whether a pesticide causes cancer or not? In weighing costs and benefits, it is important that those which are difficult to quantify are not, as a result, ignored. These are often the very things which are most crucial — such as the suffering of human beings.

It is important also that no conclusions should be drawn on the basis of 'cost-benefit ratios' which leave out the indirect costs and benefits. In a 1972 publication produced by pesticide companies, there are chapters devoted to the impact of pesticide use in the Third World. Looking, for example, at cocoa in Ghana and Nigeria, the study concludes that there was "for the two countries a benefit-cost ratio of 11-22 to 1."[2] This looks marvellous, and indeed the use of pesticides on cocoa in those countries has brought considerable benefits. But the only 'cost' included to arrive at this ratio was the foreign exchange cost of the pesticides themselves. There is no mention of the costs of transport, applica-

Robert Richter

Back-carried spray equipment. Bare arms and shoulders are exposed to pesticide.

tion, training of workers, administration and machinery. There is no examination of the effects on the health of workers, of the long-term effects on natural enemies and resistance, on the effectiveness of any vector control programme, or on the fish and wildlife.

* * * * * * *

We are aware of no cost-benefit study in a Third World country which takes full account of all the indirect or external costs and benefits. Professor David Pimentel, though, has carried out studies for the US[3] which can give us some indication of how the balance works out in a rich country. From there, we can examine the factors which might lead to different results in a poor country.

Pimentel, together with a number of colleagues, estimates present crop losses due to pests in the US at 33%, despite the application of 360 million kgs (800 million lbs) of pesticides applied to some 20% of crop acreage including pasture. Crop losses without pesticides were estimated from data from experimental field tests. These data tend to overestimate gains from pesticide use since farmers would seldom achieve the same results as those on carefully controlled experimental plots. In some cases a few readily available non-chemical controls were substituted for the chemicals removed and their costs and benefits incorporated into the analysis.

Extra crop losses, by dollar value, were calculated to be 5% of potential yield without insecticides, 3% without fungicides and 1% without herbicides. This loss of 9% of potential crop production would be added to the current 33% loss, giving a total of 42%. Calculating, for food crops only, on the basis of kilocalories of food value instead of dollar values, extra losses would be only 5% because fruits and vegetables are more expensive and more heavily treated with pesticides than the cereal crops which provide the bulk of the calorific value:

> "Based on this estimate," says Pimentel, "no serious food shortage would occur in the United States if pesticides were withdrawn because most staple foods, such as wheat, would not be greatly affected by the withdrawal of the chemicals. However, the production of certain fruits and vegetables, such as apples, peaches, onions and tomatoes would be greatly reduced."[4]

This analysis valued the extra crop losses at $8,700 million, while the costs of pesticide treatment (including application costs) were estimated at $2,200 million. This gives a financial return on pesticide use of 4 to 1. According to Pimentel other studies have arrived at similar conclusions.[5]

In considering the *indirect* costs of US pesticide use, Pimentel has included those arising from non-crop uses. The direct costs and benefits of these must therefore be included as well even though our interest is in the use of pesticides on crops. Pimentel assumed that the 200 million pounds of pesticide not used on crops in the US (vector control, nuisance pests, lawns etc) brought a similar return to those used on crops. Thus, we have *total* benefits of $10,900 million from an investment of $2,800 million.

Pimentel then went on to examine the indirect costs due to human and livestock poisoning, loss of natural enemies, resistance, loss of pollination and honey bees, fish and wildlife losses and environmental pollution. The human health effects were valued on the basis of treatment costs, plus $1 million for each life lost and $25,000 each for 0.5% of US cancer cases. The estimates for environmental and social costs were as follows:

Table 5

**Total Estimated Environmental and Social Costs
for Pesticides in the USA**

Environmental Factor	Costs ($)
Human pesticide poisonings	184,000,000
Animal pesticide poisonings and contaminated livestock products	12,000,000
Reduced natural enemies and pesticide resistance	287,000,000
Honey bee poisonings and reduced pollination	135,000,000
Losses of crops and trees	70,000,000
Fishery and wildlife losses	11,000,000
Government pesticide pollution controls	140,000,000
TOTAL	839,000,000

Source: David Pimentel el al., "Environmental and Social Costs of Pesticides: a Preliminary Assessment", *OIKOS* 34: Copenhagen, 1980, p.135.

If the amount for reduced natural enemies and resistance is excluded (since it has already been counted as a part of the direct pesticide bill) and the remainder of these costs is added to the direct costs, then the result reduces the 4 to 1 return to 3 to 1. Pimentel admits that this analysis is oversimplified and incomplete and points out that there is no satisfactory way of assessing the environmental and social costs and benefits. It is, for example, impossible to place an acceptable monetary value on human lives lost. Pimentel also points out that the values given in Table 5 "represent only a small portion of the actual costs that exist ". A more complete accounting would include, for example, unrecorded fish and wildlife losses, destruction of soil organisms and effects on the children of affected people (birth deformities etc). "If the full environmental and social costs could be measured as a whole," says Pimentel, "the total cost would probably be several times that estimated in this study."[6]

There is little doubt that the balance comes out in favour of pesticide use, but not by the kind of large margin which company statements might lead one to expect. In the Third World, though, the facts and figures are very different. Some of these differences are likely to bring a greater net benefit in the Third World while others indicate a smaller one.

On the one hand, potential benefits are greater because crop losses to pests are generally considered to be higher in the Third World. This is partly due to the relatively low level of pesticide use, but also to climatic and other conditions which favour pest development.[7] Also, the loss of part of their crop may be of greater significance to a small Third World farmer, for whom it could be a matter of life and death. Because pesticide use in the Third World is still relatively low, diminishing returns are less likely to have set in, and the Third World uses a higher proportion of insecticides, which the US study shows to produce greater savings in yield than other pesticides.

On the other hand, it is likely that a relatively high proportion of the social and environmental costs are also attributable to insecticides, of which the Third World uses a higher proportion than the US. It is fairly certain, too, that more pesticide poisoning cases occur in the Third World relative to the quantity of pesticides used, and a greater proportion of cases result in death. Resistance is likely to develop especially rapidly under Third World conditions[8] and the impact of agricultural pesticide use on malaria represents a 'cost' in the Third World which is virtually absent in the rich world.

Extra crop losses resulting from the withdrawal of pesticides would be less significant in the Third World than in Pimentel's analysis for two reasons. Firstly, the proportion of crop land treated with pesticides is generally lower than in the US, so extra losses due to their withdrawal would be lower. Secondly, Pimentel's calculations are based on results achieved by using pesticides on experimental plots. Even in the US these results are not usually achieved in farmers' fields. This is still more the case in the Third World. A survey in the Philippines showed that even farmers who are relatively well-educated and well-disposed to new technology are unable to get the most out of it.[9] Of these, 84% underdosed in their use of pesticides and all sprayed unnecessarily when growing rice varieties resistant to brown planthopper. Under these circumstances benefits in the field will be much less than those obtained on experimental plots. This is clearly demonstrated by some further figures from the Philippines. Experiments conducted at the International Rice Research Institute between 1964 and 1971 achieved yields more than double the Philippines national average, even without using insecticides. With insecticides the yields on the experimental plots were about four times the national average.[10]

* * * * * * *

The quotation at the beginning of this chapter has led us to examine the costs and benefits of existing pesticide use relative to a complete absence of pesticide use. The 'pesticide' versus 'no pesticide' discussion, though, apart from yielding no clear cut result, is essentially misleading in three very important ways. Firstly, it is unrealistic because it fails to take full account of the potential of alternative methods of pest management. Pimentel's analysis allowed for the substitution of some readily available non-chemical alternatives, but if complete withdrawal of all pesticides were to be considered, it is likely that far greater resources would be invested in researching and developing other pest management practices.

Secondly, it has been made clear in the introduction to this book that OXFAM does not advocate the complete withdrawal of all pesticides. Few others would seriously propose such a withdrawal at the present time. Therefore, while cost-benefit studies dealing with such withdrawal are useful in drawing attention to the magnitude of the problems involved in pesticide use, they compare choices which are not at present under serious consideration. The objective is rather to use pesticides in such a way that their benefit-cost ratio is improved. Policies must be adopted which will considerably reduce the human cost incurred by the problems of pesticide use in the Third World. This may entail greater restrictions on pesticide use, but not its complete abandonment.

Thirdly, the comparison of 'pesticides' with 'no pesticides' leads to a distorted view of the problem. Such comparisons imply that, in the use of pesticides, safety and health considerations are essentially in opposition to those of agricultural output and that the objective of policy is somehow to balance these

72

essentially opposing concerns. Although this may be true in certain specific instances, such as a regulatory authority considering a ban on a particularly hazardous but effective chemical, it is completely untrue for pesticide use in general. In reality, health, safety and productivity are on the same side, each tending to re-inforce the others. The real choice is between pest management practices which lead to bad control *and* devastating side effects, or pest management practices which are both safe *and* effective. The latter is in everyone's interest. Policies must be adopted urgently which will shift the balance in favour of the second. This will be the subject of Chapter 10.

* * * * * * *

The decision not to abandon pesticides altogether leads to the question how to minimise their adverse effects. This inevitably means that national or international authorities have to weigh up the costs and benefits of individual chemicals or of particular uses of each chemical. The result often involves banning or severely restricting those pesticides which are reckoned most hazardous to man or the environment and least suitable for safe and effective pest management systems. Each country must make these decisions for itself, but there are also international repercussions, in which cost-benefit considerations are absolutely central.

It is a fact that pesticides considered unsuitable in rich countries remain in use in many poor ones. Because Third World conditions differ, it is often argued that hazardous pesticides are acceptable there due to differences in the balance of costs and benefits. Third World countries, though, often lack the scientific and financial resources to carry out such assessments in order to regulate pesticide imports and use. Indeed, they may even lack the relevant legislation under which to make such regulations. In these cases, while it is reasonable to assume that different countries will have different pesticide requirements, it is dangerous to assume that pesticides restricted in Europe or North America will be acceptable in the Third World where no cost-benefit assessment has actually been made. Indeed, it is more reasonable to assume that, if a pesticide is restricted in the rich world, it will be equally unsuitable in the poor. In fact, because Third World safety precautions are less, the first assumption should be that they need stricter regulatory safeguards.

Many Third World people are worried lest it should be assumed that cost-benefit criteria will render pesticides banned in the rich countries acceptable in the Third World. Martin Kohr, Research Director of the Consumers' Association of Penang, Malaysia, puts it this way:

> "It's fine to say that some pesticides banned in the West are OK to use in Third World countries because of a difference in cost-benefit ratio - but no-one really works out the cost-benefit and makes an objective decision based on this. Decisions are actually made by companies, where no import restrictions exist, or by politicians who are often corrupt and make decisions based on the relative strength of different lobbies."[11]

If cost-benefit analyses *are* carried out, though, they can be a useful aid to policy. This was the conclusion reached by the US Agency for International Development (AID – the official US aid programme). AID have also found that the needs of their Third World partners can usually be met without resorting to pesticides banned or restricted in the US.

AID now finance the purchase of pesticides only after a cost-benefit evaluation has been carried out. The US regulatory status of the pesticide concerned determines the stringency of the analysis.[12]

Until January 1976 AID financed pesticides for the Third World with decisions on the most hazardous ones being made on a case by case basis, but without an automatic cost-benefit assessment. AID-financed pesticide exports from the US between 1969 and 1974 averaged $17.5 million (about £7 million) a year and represented 12.5% of average US pesticide exports to the Third World.[13] Between 1972 and 1976 AID-funded exports included such hazardous, banned, restricted or unregistered pesticides as heptachlor, chlordane, leptophos, endrin, dieldrin and parathion.[14]

On 3 April 1975, four US non-governmental organisations took legal action against AID for failing to fulfil the requirements of the 1969 National Environmental Policy Act by preparing an Environmental Impact Statement (EIS) on its pesticide programme.[15] As a result AID carried out an EIS. This unique study was published in May 1977 and its conclusions marked a dramatic shift in policy. AID decided to discontinue the financing of pesticides under its Commodity Import Programme except in emergencies and to subject financing of pesticides for AID projects to new procedures. The EIS compared the beneficial and adverse impacts of five alternative pest management programmes on human health, environment, economics, agriculture and social organisation. These alternatives included elimination of all pesticides from AID programmes; a restriction on pesticides banned, suspended or unregistered in the US, and leaving things as they were before the legal action.[16]

The AID study went on to identify the alternative having "the most beneficial and least adverse overall aggregate impacts on less developed countries".[17] The alternative selected was summarised as follows:

> "Alternative B will require that any proposed pesticide activity ie procurement and/or use of pesticides, be evaluated in the context of AID's overall pest management activities in a country or region. This evaluation will take into consideration the regulatory status of the pesticide [in the US] ... A risk/benefit analysis appropriate to the pesticide's regulatory status will be performed. When assistance for the pesticide is provided, it will be accompanied by sufficient technical assistance to ensure that the supplied pesticide is used safely and effectively in an environmentally acceptable manner."[18]

The AID procedures define three categories of pesticide. If the pesticide is registered for the same or similar uses without restriction in the US, a simple risk-benefit analysis is performed. If it is registered in the same way, but restricted on the basis of hazard to the user, then the analysis is backed up by a training element in the project to minimise hazards to the users. The third category includes all other pesticides, including those not registered for use in the US. For these a more stringent analysis must be carried out. This approach had been used, by September 1981, on about 50 projects over three and a half years.

> "In most cases," says AID Pest Management Specialist Fred Whittemore, "we were able to meet mission and project

requirements with pesticides from category 1, although occasionally we do have to fall back to a pesticide in category 2... We have had only one occasion to use a pesticide not registered by EPA."[19]

These procedures together with other policies adopted as a result of the EIS, represent a highly commendable and rational procedure aimed at safeguarding the interests of Third World people. A small example of the operation of the AID procedures serves to illustrate their usefulness to Third World countries.

In March 1979, the Panama Government asked AID to spend $30,000 (£15,000) on eleven different pesticides for distribution to 275 small growers. A consultant visited Panama to evaluate the health and environmental risks of the pesticides, which included endrin and heptachlor. The review recommended the use of alternative pesticides which were less toxic and not restricted in the US. Panama accepted this recommendation. Also the growers receive instructions on application methods and are supplied with appropriate protective clothing.[20]

AID's system may not be perfect — it is, like any system, subject to human error or abuse   but it is better for the Third World than any of the others considered in the EIS. There seems to be no reason why UK and EEC aid programmes should not adopt similar procedures. In Britain, the expertise exists within the Overseas Development Administration (ODA) itself, in the form of the Centre for Overseas Pest Research, as well as in universities, such as London's Imperial College, to carry out effectively the necessary studies, and to give the follow-up technical support.

Aid programmes, though, account for only a relatively small proportion of total pesticide exports. At a US conference in 1979, one of the speakers stressed the significance of this.

"The regular commercial channels supply 16 times the amount
of chemicals provided by the direct government assistance programs.
The policies that have received the greatest attention, however,
have been those that most directly affect the 6% rather than the
94%. Future policies and regulations should take cognizance of
this."[21]

Pesticides exported by the private sector have a similar potential to damage the health and livelihoods of the poor if used indiscriminately. If the safety and effectiveness of pesticides funded by aid programmes are best safeguarded by selective cost-benefit evaluations, then such evaluations could have an equal value if carried out for the supply of pesticides by the private sector.

Such procedures though may be prohibitively expensive and time consuming if applied even to selected commercial exports. Nevertheless, some safeguards in the commercial sector could be initiated. These could include packaging and labelling requirements and consultation and exchange of information between exporting and importing countries. These measures would at least enhance the importing government's ability to make an informed and realistic assessment and even to have the export stopped prior to shipment. The question of control of commercial pesticide exports is discussed in detail in Chapter 11.

* * * * * * *

75

While regulatory authorities can make broad decisions to ban or restrict certain pesticides, the final decision remains with the farmer. No authority can carry out a cost-benefit analysis for every farmer's field, or even for every region of a country. Ideally regulations at international and national level would prevent the most inappropriate chemicals from reaching the farmer. The farmer's own decisions, though, still have a crucial bearing on the safety and efficacy of pesticide use. In making these decisions the farmer depends on the advice and information he or she receives from extension services, labels and company promotional activities. The farmer can accurately assess the costs and benefits of his or her own pesticide use only if this advice and information is full and accurate.

In this context it is interesting to look at some 'cost-benefit' studies of pesticide use from the farm-level perspective. These studies exclude social and environmental costs and so are more in the nature of investment appraisals. The ICAITI report, firstly, examined pesticide use in Central American cotton by two methods. One was a straight forward economic analysis of the type and level of pesticide use, and the second was a comparison with integrated pest management.

The ICAITI report carried out a statistical analysis of existing farm and county data on levels of pesticide use in Nicaragua. The relationships of a number of factors with cotton yields were assessed and it was found that "yields depended to a large extent on the use of pesticides". As pesticide use increases, the yield increase resulting from the last pound of pesticide decreases — an example of diminishing returns. From the strictly financial point of view of the farmer, the optimum level is where the last pound brings about a yield increase of a value equal to the cost of that pound of pesticide. Any pesticide use above that level would be counterproductive and wasteful. Taking account of indirect costs, even this 'optimum' is too high. Even so, average use levels in Nicaragua were found to be just above the estimated optimum and "in most important cotton growing areas pesticide use is well above the optimum". Applying the optimum derived in Nicaragua more broadly in Central America (Nicaragua, Guatemala, El Salvador and Honduras), ICAITI found that in 1974/5 average pesticide use levels were 38% above the optimum and that farmers' profits would be improved by a rational reduction in pesticide use.

Technical assistance from extension services was found to increase production and the use of integrated pest management techniques were found to produce higher profits with 40% less pesticide application. IPM also stresses the use of low toxicity products and reduces social and environmental costs.

Why, then, did farmers use too much of the most hazardous pesticides? Factors influencing use levels were found to include price, sales efforts by companies, information and technical assistance, fertiliser use, and farm size. Higher prices and technical assistance discourage use while the other factors encourage it.

Thus, while company promotional efforts can result in farmers using excessive amounts of hazardous pesticides, good technical assistance, especially that stressing the techniques of IPM, helps farmers to achieve a more optimal level of pesticide use.[22]

A study in Bangladesh points out another important factor. Even if pesticide use yields a net benefit, it may be that an even higher net benefit could be gained by investing the same scarce resources in some other input such as fertiliser or irrigation. The profitability of pesticide use therefore provides only part of the information the farmer needs to make a decision.

This study found that the cost-benefit ratios (excluding social and environmental costs and benefits) depended on four factors: the cost of protection; the resulting yield increase; the level of the rice yield, and the price of rice. These vary from field to field, farm to farm and year to year.[23]

At 1975 price levels it would pay to protect average yielding rice only when pest losses were over 20%. The study concludes that:

"There is no such thing as *a* cost-benefit ratio except for given circumstances. There are many cost-benefit ratios. However, it can be generalised that at a price of 120 taka it seldom pays to protect rice crops with average or lower than average yields. This may account for the general lack of treatment by farmers.... the average cost-benefit ratio is essentially 1 to 1."[24]

The implication of this is that farmers who already achieve high yields due to irrigation, good soil, fertiliser, high yielding varieties, etc, are likely to gain most from pesticide use, while the poorer farmers, who attain low yields of low value crops, are most unlikely to benefit from pesticide use.

* * * * * * *

The examination of costs and benefits of pesticide use, then, show a number of things. First, that the attempt to balance total costs and benefits against a no-pesticide alternative is essentially a red herring which anyway yields no clear-cut result. Second, that cost-benefit analysis can be a useful aid to regulatory decision-making, but only if it is properly planned and executed.

Our discussion demonstrates also the crucial need for international co-operation and sharing of information, and the potential benefit of careful environmental assessment of pesticides prior to their export to the Third World. If the Third World's poor farmers and farmworkers are to reap maximum benefits from pesticide use rather than to pay its costs in health without benefit, it is essential that pesticide exporting countries provide full information and help to ensure that alternative options are fully explored, and potential hazards assessed.

The importance of farmers' and farmworkers' perceptions and the critical role of full and correct information in promotional and technical assistance activities have also been seen.

The last point, illustrated by the Bangladesh study, is that the costs and benefits of pesticide use are not distributed evenly throughout a society. The costs and benefits may be paid and reaped by different people.

It cannot be argued that *any* costs of pesticides use are justified in terms of feeding the hungry unless it can be demonstrated that it is the hungry who reap the benefits. Already we have shown in Bangladesh that it is likely to be the richer farmer who has the most to gain from using pesticides. In the next chapter we examine this issue in more detail.

How the Costs and Benefits are Distributed

the Effect on the Poorest

HOW THE COSTS AND BENEFITS ARE DISTRIBUTED

How far do pesticides contribute to the alleviation of hunger in the Third World? What has been the impact of pesticide use on the poor -- the small and marginal cultivators and landless labourers? The kind of cost-benefit calculations which have been examined so far do not give the answers to these crucial questions. In order to find these answers, it is necessary to know how the costs and benefits are distributed in present Third World societies.

The distribution of the costs and benefits of any technological change depends essentially on the way in which society is organised and on the wider technological context. In examining the economic and social impact of pesticides, therefore, it is necessary to discuss a range of topics which are not directly associated with pesticide use but which nevertheless have a bearing on the impact of pesticides.

The pesticide technology interacts with other technologies in a social and economic context. It is largely the social conditions which determine the distribution of pesticide costs and benefits, not vice-versa. In discussing inequitable systems of distribution, it should be made clear that these do not *result* from the use of pesticides.

Nevertheless, within a given socio-economic system, different technologies may have characteristics which make them more or less likely to benefit the poor. A technology may be more or less 'appropriate' to the needs and abilities of the poor in a particular society. Pesticides, like any other new technology introduced into the Third World, have inevitably become a part of the interaction between rich and poor, locally and internationally.

It is apparent that the benefits will not necessarily accrue to the same people or social groups who pay the costs. Unless they are exceptionally enlightened, though, farmers will make their pesticide use decisions on the basis of the costs and benefits accruing to themselves, rather than to society as a whole, or the poor and hungry in particular.

In Britain and the rich world some mechanisms exist by which the decision-maker must take at least some account of the costs accruing to other individuals or to society as a whole. For example, an employer may have to continue to pay a sick worker, or pay compensation in the case of industrial injury. In other

Farm labourers are at the leading edge of the application of pesticides. Safe use is difficult when spraying rice with hand-held pressure hoses.

cases the bill is paid by society and legislation enacted to prevent the 'cost' occurring. For example, a farmworker in Britain who is poisoned by a pesticide would receive free treatment under the National Health Service, while the Health and Safety Regulations exist to prevent the poisoning occurring in the first place.

In the Third World such means of redistributing 'costs' often do not exist or are not enforced. If farm labour is plentiful and no sickness benefit or compensation has to be paid by the farmer, then the poisoning of a worker may hardly enter into the calculations of the employer. In such a case, the worker will often have to bear the entire costs arising from his or her own injury, especially any loss of earnings. In Central America in 1977 out of El Salvador, Guatemala, Honduras and Nicaragua only Guatemala had any social security programme covering agricultural workers.[1] Even the existence of such a programme is no guarantee that the worker will benefit from it.

In the Third World, then, it is reasonable to assume that the full costs are borne by those on whom they initially fall, and by their families.

Who Pays the Costs?

The direct costs are borne by the users of the pesticides -- who also reap the immediate benefits. But who pays the indirect social and environmental costs of Third World pesticide use? Although different countries and regions have different cultures, traditions, climates, cropping and landholding patterns, and social and political systems, it is possible to draw upon examples from different regions in an attempt to build up a general picture.

The first indirect 'costs' are those resulting from accidental and occupational pesticide poisoning. In Central America, for example, the ICAITI report found that the people most affected by pesticide poisoning were young adult males

79

between 16 and 35, "the majority of them temporary day labourers engaged in cotton harvesting".[2] In a 1973 study of 243 poisoning cases in Nicaragua, 170 were day labourers.[3] For these people lack of education and literacy combines with inadequate access to protective clothing to increase the likelihood of poisoning. In Central America, at least, the poorest people in the cotton environment are the ones most likely to bear the cost of poisoning. Amongst those areas where agriculture is largely a matter of growing cash crops, often for export, on relatively large landholdings there seems to be no reason to assume that Central American cotton is an exception. The poor everywhere have least access to knowledge and equipment which could safeguard them from poisoning, and they are likely to be especially susceptible due to greater exposure and general ill-health.

In the more traditional kind of Third World agriculture, where staple food crops are grown by family cultivators, we have less information, but again the smaller, poorer cultivators and the landless labourers are likely to be more susceptible where they are pesticide users. In Sri Lanka (population 14.3 million in 1978), where there are 14,000 poisoning cases a year, most of the pesticides are used by smallholders growing rice and vegetables.[4] The tea plantations, once the biggest users, have adopted less chemical-reliant methods. Our visits to small cultivators in 1980 indicated that they were very much aware of pesticides, and most were pesticide users. The poorest cultivators are the most likely to be using poorly maintained equipment and to lack the training and literacy which could safeguard their health.

In Chapter 3 it was shown how agricultural pesticide use accelerated the resurgence of malaria. This indirect 'cost' of pesticide use will be borne by the victims of malaria. Poor people, already weakened by parasites and malnutrition, are less likely to survive malaria attacks[5] and the effect of malaria also reduces agricultural productivity. This is especially serious for the small cultivator who relies on family labour, and the landless labourer who loses income.

The rural poor are also likely to suffer most from both pesticide poisoning and malaria because they lack access to health care services which could effectively treat these conditions. In rural India for example one government health centre with two doctors may have to serve more than 120,000 people in over 100 villages. Even those health services which do exist are rarely geared to treating occupational health problems such as pesticide poisoning.[6]

The environmental 'costs' also hit the poor hardest. It is the small self-provisioning farmer, for example, who relies most on the protein provided by paddy-field fish.

The 'cost' of the resistance of pests to pesticides and the destruction of the natural enemies of pests by the pesticides is borne initially by the purchaser who must apply more, and more expensive, pesticides. These costs may then be passed on to the consumer or the worker through prices and wages. The treadmill also adds to the other indirect costs.

The 'cost' of residues in food falls on local consumers, rich and poor, and on the farmers (and their employees) growing cash crops for export.

In the Third World the poor invariably suffer most from any contingency. The indirect costs of pesticide use are no exception. It is sometimes said that the poor are not affected by pesticides because they cannot afford to use them.

This is incorrect because the indirect costs are not borne in full by the purchaser but also by employees, consumers and the community at large. Moreover, it is no longer true to say that small and marginal farmers never buy pesticides.

Who Reaps the Benefits?

In discussing who benefits from the application of the pesticide technology to Third World agriculture, it is helpful to see these agricultural systems as what Andrew Pearse, of the UN Research Institute for Social Development (UNRISD), calls 'bi-modal'.[7] In much of the Third World two kinds of agriculture exist side by side, although they merge and inter-relate in many ways. In the extreme cases there is, at one end, a large-scale farm producing crops for cash sale and perhaps for export, and owned by a rich landowner, possibly living in the city. At the other extreme is the small, self-provisioning cultivator growing mainly staple food crops for the family or the village. For the sake of simplicity we will call these 'commercial' and 'traditional' respectively. They are distinguished by the degree to which they are involved in the market, the size of economic units, the crops grown and methods used, and the social position of those who control them.

The 'Commercial' Sector

There is no doubt that most pesticide use in the Third World is in the commercial sector. William Furtick of the FAO and Professor Ray F. Smith explain:

"It is clear that in the past, nearly all agricultural use of pesticides in developing countries has been on cash crops, with cotton representing at least half of all use. Plantation crops such as sugar-cane and tree crops have been major consumers of pesticides with vegetables, rice and maize, when they are raised as cash crops, of lesser but increasing importance."[8]

It is evident that a large proportion of these cash crops are exported. In Central America in 1970, for example, about 80% of agricultural output by value was exported.[9] In addition, many cash crops are sold on the domestic market to better-off consumers. Either way, extra production resulting from the application of pesticides brings no direct increase in the supply of food available to the poor.

In the case of plantation crops, the direct beneficiaries of any yield increase are the large landowners who constitute the wealthiest section of Third World societies. In India in 1970, for example, a third of the croplands were owned by the wealthiest 5% of the rural population.[10]

Cotton, the major consumer of pesticides in the Third World, is not really a food crop, although it is a source of edible oil and of animal feed, used in particular for beef production. Little of the latter, though, helps to feed local people. In Latin America, for example, almost half the beef is exported to the rich world while much of the remainder is consumed by the richer members of local society.

In Indonesia estate-style farms growing coconuts, coffee, sugar-cane and rubber for export consume 20 times as much pesticide as used by smallholders growing food for local markets.[11]

It is apparent then that a large proportion of pesticides used in the Third World contribute little directly to local food supply. The direct beneficiaries would appear to be rich world consumers and the large landowners and better-off

81

consumers of the Third World.

Many Third World countries, though, remain critically dependent on cash crop exports to richer countries as a source of foreign exchange. Such dependence brings difficulties in terms of price fluctuations in international markets and some countries are making efforts to diversify their agriculture and increase food self-reliance. In addition foreign exchange may be spent on foreign investment, luxury imports and industrial development, rather than on capital equipment and rural development. For these reasons it cannot be assumed that the growth of production in the commercial sector benefits the poor or feeds the hungry.

Commercial agriculture provides employment to some poor people and many rely on seasonal work on large farms to supplement their incomes. But the growth of the commercial sector can also threaten those incomes by reducing the land available for small food crop farmers. In Nicaragua between 1952 and 1967, for example, cotton acreage increased four times while acreage of basic grains was cut in half.[12] In addition, the jobs which the poor are forced by necessity to take on the commercial farms are too often poorly paid and hazardous, and subject the workers to appalling living conditions.

Where the commercial sector produces food crops, often for export to the rich world, a part of their pesticide use is based not on any nutritional consideration, but on the desire to produce a perfect-looking, blemish-free product. In the US it has been estimated that as much as 16% of insecticides used on fruit and vegetables are used for such 'cosmetic' purposes.[13] The rich world consumer has conflicting demands. He or she wants food of perfect appearance, but also free of excessive pesticide residues. While the former takes priority then the "quality standards of an affluent society"[14] will influence management decisions on the Third World's commercial farms. The result is an increase in pesticide use, a greater risk of poisoning for the farm labourer and all the other side effects of excessive pesticide use.

While most pesticides are used in the commercial sector, it cannot legitimately be argued that Third World pesticide use helps to reduce hunger and malnutrition. To feed the hungry it is necessary to put into the hands of the poor the power to grow or buy the food they need. Pesticides are a central part of a Third World commercial agriculture which often fails to do this.

The 'Traditional' Sector

Although the majority of pesticides, as we have seen, are being used in the commercial sector, they are also an increasingly common part of the lives of poor cultivators. The small cultivator's decision whether or not to use pesticides depends on many factors. Three of the most important are the crop being grown, the cost of the pesticides and access to water. The farmer on well-watered land can grow high yielding varieties of high value crops on which the cost of pesticides can be justified in economic terms. For farmers growing low value crops such as millet, sorghum and cassava, pesticide use is less economic.[15]

Where small farmers grow higher value crops, though, pesticide use is no longer uncommon. Preliminary results of a sample survey in West Orissa, India, show that about a quarter of landowning households growing fruits and vegetables may be pesticide users. Gaisillat Block, where this survey was carried out, belongs to the subsistence farming economy in the poorest area of the poorest State in India. Thirty-one households in the survey used pesticides, including parathion (5 households). This included over a third of the big farmers, 28% of the small farmers and 11% of the marginal farmers.[16] So, even in the poorest areas, a significant proportion even of small and marginal farmers, at least those growing fruit and vegetables, use pesticides. But the larger the farmer the more likely he or she is to use pesticides. Because small farmer pesticide use is so closely linked to the size of holding, access to water and so on, it is difficult to examine the distribution of the benefits of pesticide use outside the wider context of the rest of the agricultural and social systems. In the last twenty years or so these systems have been subjected to many changing circumstances, not least of which has been the arrival of the new technology of the Green Revolution . Pesticides are an important part of these changes and part of the package of inputs needed by farmers if they are to get the most from the new seed strains of the Green Revolution. These seeds, especially in the earlier days, were particularly susceptible to pest attack and so required the application of pesticides if they were to deliver their full potential. The new seeds also required inputs of fertilizer and the resulting commercialization of traditional agriculture, and contact with suppliers of inputs added further to the likelihood of pesticide use. As a result of these connections, a large proportion of the pesticides used in the 'traditional' sector is probably used in the context of the Green Revolution package in maize, rice and wheat. An examination of pesticide use in the context of the Green Revolution can therefore throw some light on the possible distributional effects of pesticide use among Third World food crop farmers.

The Green Revolution

The use of 'high-yielding varieties' (HYVs) can intensify pest problems.[17] The Green Revolution has led to relatively large areas being planted with a single variety of a single crop providing ideal conditions for pests to which the variety is susceptible. Secondly, the use of relatively large amounts of fertilizer produces luxuriant growth which can support a greater pest population. Thirdly, the varieties themselves are often less resistant to pest attack than the hardy traditional varieties they replace.

> "The development of modern crop production and protection technology," say Norton and Conway, "has therefore been an interactive and cumulative process... The result has been a system of food production that critically depends upon the use of pesticides."[18]

Only those who adopt the Green Revolution technology package of which pesticides are an integral part stand to gain from it. But these gains will vary according to other conditions and the mere adoption of the package is no guarantee of benefit. Also, those who do not adopt it are not free of the repercussions of the new technology which affects the supply and demand for food, land and labour. In determining the impact of the Green Revolution on the poor, these are the three main factors to be considered: who adopts; who benefits most from adoption, and what is the effect on those who do not adopt. The first two overlap, since those with most to gain are most likely to adopt.

The rate of adoption of HYVs has been very variable. This depends for example on the availability of water, a critical factor in the success of the new technology. The better-off farmers who can afford well-watered land are more likely to

adopt the new varieties and so have more to gain from the application of pesticides.
Because the new varieties require more purchased inputs — seed, fertilizer, pesticides — the benefits to farmers depend on their access to working capital. This usually means borrowing and the poor farmers find it more difficult to get credit and may have to pay higher rates of interest. So the poor respond least to, and gain least from the new technology.[19] Access to credit is an important factor in determining the pattern of pesticide use. Farmers with greater access are more likely to be able to reap the benefits which pesticides can bring. The input needs of the Green Revolution and the requirement for new knowledge mean that the cultivator must act in the market, must sell some of the harvest to buy inputs like pesticides and must find access to credit, advice and services. In all these spheres the poor, small cultivator is at a disadvantage.

"Peasants may find themselves competitors for credit or irrigation facilities with agriculturalists who have city houses and political connections," says Andrew Pearse of UNRISD. "Poor villagers may have to compete for institutional credit with the local elite who make up the village committees that allocate the credit; illiterate, ill-clad cultivators may have to argue their case in town offices with status-conscious officials."[20]

Pearse calls this the "talents effect", "the interplay of the social and the economic that tends to strengthen the rich and enrich the powerful, as well as to weaken the poor and impoverish the weak".[21]

For the landless labourer the Green Revolution technology leads to two opposing trends. On the one hand, the new technology requires more labour per hectare (but less labour per hundredweight of output). On the other hand, the consolidation of landholdings and increasing use of tractors, both growing out of the new technology of the Green Revolution, have displaced labour.[22] The uniformity of HYVs have facilitated mechnisation, and in the Philippines between 1966 and 1970 labour requirement per ton of rice fell from 34 to 25 person-days. In some cases too, increased fertilizer use has led to worse weed problems. But herbicides are often used instead of labour.
The US Agency for International Development recognises the problem:

"In LDCs, where unemployment is a major problem and a large percentage of the labour force works in agriculture, the use of chemical pesticides may displace labour in the field, adding to unemployment."[23]

To summarise, then, the Green Revolution has been generally successful in increasing production but it has tended to increase inequalities between social classes and between regions, sometimes actually making the very poor worse off. In regions better endowed with irrigation and fertile land, even relatively poor farmers have benefited. In some places employment and wages have risen. But the general effect has been one of patchy and precarious achievements in a sea of poverty.

After some ten years of study of the Green Revolution by UNRISD and the UN "Global Two" Study, Pearse draws this devastating conclusion:

"Where inequalities exist already, the green revolutionists' strategy results in the persistence and generation of poverty for the majority of the people in rural areas."[24]

84

In so far as pesticides are used in the context of the commercial sector or the Green Revolution it cannot confidently be said that they have contributed to improving the livelihoods of the poor or to feeding the hungry. In some cases, together with the rest of the technology package, they appear to have achieved exactly the opposite.

For the richer farmers and landowners, payment of the direct costs of pesticide use has brought them immediate, though not unqualified, benefits. These have, though, largely failed to trickle down to the poor who have borne the greater share of the indirect social and environmental costs and who may even have been put at a greater disadvantage in their society than ever.

The pesticide technology itself cannot bear the full blame for the way in which its costs and benefits have been distributed. It is the economic, social and political reality in which the technology has to operate which determines who gains and who loses. Under the appropriate social conditions the well-regulated application of the pesticide technology could bring greater benefits to the poor.

Many of the changes which would help the poor to gain from the pesticide technology can only be brought about by the governments of Third World countries themselves. But even in these cases, the rich world could often help through its aid programmes. These policies would include diversifying agriculture to reduce dependence on the export of a narrow range of cash crops. In the meantime, much could be done, as discussed in earlier chapters, to encourage a more sensible approach to pest management in the production of these crops.

Other policies which would help the poor to benefit from new technology would involve reducing inequalities in, for example, education and land ownership.[25] If this were combined with policies to improve poor farmers' access to credit, water supply and inputs, then the small farmers would be in a much better position to benefit from pesticides and other new technology. This would also necessitate great improvements in the methods of passing on new techniques to the farmers, such as through improvements in agricultural extension services.

Such changes in Third World agricultural development policies should ideally operate alongside changes in the *technology* which is developed and promoted. HYVs have tended to be more susceptible to pest damage and to respond well under optimal conditions. Varieties designed for pest resistance and for a good response under adverse conditions would help to offset the advantage of those who have preferential access to inputs. Such varieties are not without problems (pests can, for example, overcome the resistance of crop varieties) but the research institutes which have pioneered the Green Revolution are now putting more emphasis on resistant varieties and alternative pest management techniques.

Pest control cannot be seen as an isolated technique. It must be seen as a part of an agricultural and social system, and fitted, where possible, into more integrated development programmes. The need is to devise and apply technologies so that they will *assist* development, so that the interaction between technology and social change is of benefit to the poor.

In the case of pesticides a first step would be to regulate the use of the most hazardous pesticides and to encourage the timely application of minimum doses of the safest effective chemicals. Ideally, pesticides should be used in conjunction with pest resistant varieties, in the context of integrated pest management programmes geared specifically to the needs of small farmers.

Such an approach should try to build on the farmers' knowledge of the land and the local ecosystem and on traditional pest management techniques.

Where the technology is not appropriate to the needs and abilities of the poor, then special care is needed to communicate the measures necessary for safety and efficacy.

Mixing DDT in Africa. Unsafe mixing techniques and lack of protective clothing expose workers to serious risks.

The next chapter examines how pesticides are promoted and labelled in the Third World, and the need for changes in these practices. Chapter 10 looks at alternative pest management methods and how they can help the poor. If the measures advocated in these and other chapters are not adopted, then the present maldistribution of costs and benefits will continue. Unless changes are made it may not be far from the truth to say that, rather than feeding the hungry, pesticides will be poisoning the hungry to feed the well-fed.

Advertising, Promotion and Labelling

ADVERTISING, PROMOTION AND LABELLING

Pesticides, essentially products of western technology, can be extremely hazardous. The conditions for the safe and effective use of this technology are not always present even in the rich world; in the Third World they are often a distant dream. In the words of one pesticide company executive:

"We have not been completely successful in harmonizing pesticide technology with the cultural forces and values of our own society. It is proving infinitely more difficult to achieve a successful accommodation of pesticide technology with the cultures and economies of the lesser developed countries."[1]

It has been seen in this book how problems arise from the relatively uncontrolled sale and use of an inappropriate and potentially dangerous technology. There are two kinds of problems: those resulting from the toxicity of the chemicals and those resulting from the ability of pests to develop resistance. There are two important methods for preventing the occurrence of these problems. One is good and effective legislation at international and national level. This will be discussed further in Chapter 11. The other is the provision of usable and full information to farmers and farmworkers. All channels for conveying such information should be responsibly employed as a means of prevention of poisoning, resistance and environmental damage, ie to promote the safe and effective use of pesticides. There are three main channels by which information about pesticides currently reaches users (sometimes via shop-keepers):

— official advice and extension services
— pesticide labels
— company sales promotion.

These channels all too often fail to provide information to the user. Extension services in most countries are inadequate, overstretched and under-financed. In poor countries with limited resources this is almost unavoidable, although improvements could certainly be made. Labels are very often in the wrong language or give insufficient or even false information. Company sales promotions are often sophisticated and well financed and in many countries appear to be the most effective channel for reaching the farmer. It is therefore absolutely crucial that sales promotions are used not merely to sell a product, but to provide usable information on pesticide safety and pest management. In fact, the opposite is very often the case.

The provision of information is of little use if it is not *usable* information. For written information to be usable requires literacy. For advice about the use of protective equipment to be usable the equipment must be available and within financial reach. This requires the farmer to have access to money or credit. Advice to workers applying pesticides can only be adopted, even if it reaches the worker, if the worker has sufficient negotiating power to affect the instructions of his or her employer. It is no good telling workers only to spray in the early morning if they are ordered to spray all day by an employer who can easily replace them if they disobey. Employees can only use information if they have job security and negotiating power. Similarly it is no good telling someone to wash with soap and water immediately after spraying, if it is a mile to the nearest water supply and they cannot afford soap. The water supply may even be a pesticide-contaminated irrigation ditch, as in the cotton fields of Central America.[2]

Information is fully usable then only where the following conditions are met:

- literacy
- availability of protective equipment
- availability of money or credit
- negotiating power
- job security
- access to clean water.

For most Third World pesticide users, especially for small farmers and landless labourers, these conditions do not exist and are not likely to do so in the foreseeable future. These are social and economic conditions which will be achieved only through the long-term process of development. In other words, under present circumstances in the Third World, pesticides are a text-book case of inappropriate technology. This imposes a heavy responsibility on all those engaged in the propagation of this technology. Mr Frederick J. Rarig, Vice-President of the Rohm and Haas Company recognizes this responsibility:

"The pesticide industry of the US must either cease to do business in countries that do not meet basic safety standards or it must assume responsibility for securing observance of these standards by its customers in these countries while it works with the governments of these countries and international and regional trade and standards groups to develop effective controls of production, formulation, use, and disposal and effective enforcement of these controls."[3]

The difficulties involved in safe and effective use of pesticides in the Third World, and in communicating usable information to farmers, are no excuse for not trying. In fact they are the opposite. The difficulties accentuate the necessity to ensure that the pesticides used are the most suitable for the job, taking account of health and resistance problems and the difficulties in preventing them. It is necessary to ensure that the maximum information is supplied to farmers by all possible channels, that maximum use is made of non-chemical methods of pest management and that pesticide use is kept to the minimum consistent with a reasonable degree of plant protection.

Labelling

The label is the final and most direct instruction to the user of a pesticide. It should give the user all the information necessary to enable him or her to apply the pesticide in the safest and most efficacious manner possible. This is not always satisfactorily achieved. The first problem is lack of safety information on labels. Responses to an OXFAM questionnaire indicate that labels often fail to give details of necessary safety procedures. An entomologist in the Gambia, for example, writes:

"Often drums are marked only with the name of the chemical and its formulation; rarely is further information included as to dosages or safety."

It has been reported that a recent check in Mexico found that 50% of the pesticides sold there were incorrectly labelled.[4] In a number of countries we have reports of pesticides on sale in unlabelled plastic bags, or bags giving absolutely no precautions. Some bags even fail to identify the product inside. We have one bag from Botswana which names the contents as "Daconil", a *fungicide*. Beneath this it says: "sprayable *insecticide* for vegetables". The caution is in English and Swarti - - the language of Swaziland (a country 300 miles away).

A team from the International Rice Research Institute recently carried out a survey of herbicide labels in the Philippines. They concluded that "many labels did not meet basic information requirements". Among their recommendations was one for a minimum set of safety precautions.[5]

In assessing the usefulness of labels, it would be useful to have some internationally accepted guidelines with which to compare the reality. Sufficiently detailed and widely agreed guidelines of this type do not at present exist, but some efforts have been made which indicate the general nature of effective pesticide labelling.

The ILO Code of Practice on Safety and Health in Agricultural Work was first published in 1965. The code is intended to guide the relevant bodies all over the world and covers hazards of buildings, machinery, electricity etc, and also deals with standards of accommodation and health care. It is, therefore, not sufficiently specific to act as a definitive statement on pesticide labelling. The relevant section, on 'dangerous substances' covers fertilizers and other products as well as pesticides and contains just one clause on labelling. This is as follows:

"523. (1) All containers of toxic substances should state on the label - -

(a) the safety of precautions to be taken in handling and use;
(b) the nature of the early symptoms indicative of poisoning;
(c) the immediate first-aid method to be instituted in the event of over-exposure and suitable antidotes, and
(d) an indication of the methods of safe disposal of containers.

(2) These labels should be approved by the competent national authority."[6]

In 1977 ILO published Guidelines on the Safe Use of Pesticides. The relevant clause in these Guidelines adds to the above that labels should be in local language and that the active ingredient should be specified. Under 'Duties of manufacturers' it states that they should ensure that every product distributed

"bears a label which is in accordance with the requirements of the national authorities, and which gives in the language of the region, comprehensive instructions for safe use, warns of possible hazards, specifies the active ingredients and gives guidelines for first aid in case of poisoning (including antidotes) ".[7]

89

Labelling has also been discussed under the auspices of FAO in the course of discussions about the international standardisation of pesticide registration requirements. At a 1977 meeting in Rome a committee on labelling went into considerable detail concerning the importance of labels and the material which should be included. They concluded with a proposal that an expert group should

"be convened as a matter of urgency to develop 'Guidelines on Good Labelling Practice' for adoption and use by industry and registration authorities".[8]

These Guidelines are apparently being drawn up by FAO, but, at the time of writing, work has not been completed. The guidelines will, it is hoped, include information on readability, print size, colour contrasts, the use of symbols and standard phrases etc, as well as on content. They should also be as strong and binding as possible and perhaps could be incorporated with a similar code on advertising.

Bearing in mind the guidelines which already exist, let us look at the current situation, and at a few specific labels.

Banpot Napompeth, Director of Thailand's National Biological Control Research Center has described the situation in his country:

"In spite of existing laws and regulation," he says, "labels do not include necessary information on active ingredients, and usually no antidote nor first aid instruction are given. There is no specification given whether the formulation is for household use or for field pests. Information of residual life is generally lacking."[9]

Many labels in many countries conform to this description, especially those of pesticides formulated or re-packed by local distributors. The international companies, though, sometimes fail to give label information in all the relevant local languages. This may be more difficult in some places where a number of languages are spoken, but it can and should be done. If labels are not in the language of the particular user then all further guidelines on their content become effectively irrelevant.

From Botswana, for example, we have labels printed only in English and Afrikaans, for chemicals distributed by South African associates of Shell and Hoechst. Hoechst point out that they do not sell this product to Botswana farmers directly.[10] There are no trade barriers between Botswana and South Africa and these products may have been purchased in South Africa. They include some highly toxic products for which safety depends on instructions being followed to the letter, such as endosulfan (Hoechst), dieldrin and mevinphos (Shell). Dieldrin is no longer permitted for agricultural use in the EEC, including Britain. It is classified by WHO as "extremely hazardous". Not only is it sold by Shell South Africa in Botswana, it is not labelled in the local African language. Mevinphos, sold by Shell in Botswana under the trade name "Phosdrin 2" is also classified by WHO as "extremely hazardous". In Britain it is covered by Health and Safety Regulations requiring the wearing of protective clothing. Yet this too is sold in Botswana with no directions in local language. Dr. Joyce Tait, a lecturer at the Open University, has made a study of farmers' perceptions about pesticides. Concerning Phosdrin, she says:

"Many of the farmers I've spoken to in Britain regard Phosdrin as too dangerous to be handled by amateurs, even with protective clothing."[11]

In Botswana there are two official languages. One of these is English, but there are nevertheless literate people who read only the local African language (Setswana). Where it is *so* crucial that instructions are understood, and where they may require more than basic literacy, it is surely essential that the local language should be used as well as English. Shell pointed out that Botswana is a small market but nevertheless agreed seriously to consider the use of Setswana on labels for use in Botswana. However, Mr B.N. Fox of Shell subsequently advised OXFAM that after local enquiries it had been decided that "the inclusion of use instructions in Setswana would be superfluous. Both products are used in minimal quantities annually on crops which are only grown in English and Afrikaan speaking areas."[12]

In a remote area on the border of Tamil Nadu and Andhra Pradesh in India, we found pesticides such as phosphamidon and methyl parathion in use. Both of these are classified by WHO as "extremely hazardous". The phosphamidon (Dimecron) label which we saw gave instructions only in English and Hindi (the local language is Tamil) and referred the reader to an accompanying folder. In response to our enquiry on this matter, Ciba-Geigy sent a copy of the label and leaflet currently in use in India. This label gives basic information in 12 languages (including Tamil). The folder, in 13 languages, gives safety instructions described by Ciba-Geigy as "sufficiently comprehensive".[13] Even this folder, though, failed to give information on waiting periods, keeping livestock out of treated areas or danger to bees. It also failed to recommend protective clothing. Ciba-Geigy have now stated that,

> "our affiliate company in India intends to include the additional safety instructions on the folder in the sense suggested by Oxfam".[14]

These labels also raise the question of how far the information they contain is actually usable. The phosphamidon label specified an antidote "altropine+2PAM" and said "in case of accident call physician". It is extremely unlikely that any physician would be contactable in remote areas like this one within a number of hours. The local clinic had never heard of 2PAM and certainly would not have it in stock.

The difficulties involved in following label precautions are graphically described by Deanna Donovan, a US forestry specialist working in Nepal. She accompanied her night watchman, Hem Bahadur (who was introduced in Chapter 1), to a local shop where he wished to purchase an insecticide. Offered a bottle by the shopkeeper, Deanna read the instruction leaflet:

> "I was horrified. The manufacturer strongly recommended that the user ... wear rubber gloves, high rubber boots and preferably goggles and an air purification mask. When incredulously I asked if the shop rented or sold this equipment or if it could be purchased in Kathmandu, the several men behind the counter laughed heartily...

> To every customer he offered the same poison he had offered me. As I walked out of the shop I saw several of the instruction leaflets from these bottles littering the ground. The illustrated pamphlet wrapped around the bottle was printed in Nepali as well as English. Roughly eighty percent of the population of this mountain kingdom is illiterate... Should the purchaser comprehend the precautionary measures recommended, it would be all but impossible to buy or rent the equipment necessary to carry out the instructions."[15]

Victims of poisoning cannot call a doctor as labels recommend if there is not one available. On average, for the poorest 38 countries in the world, there is only one doctor for every 10,000 people — and most of those are in urban areas. In Nepal, for example, there are only about 400 doctors for the entire population of 13.6 million.[16]

There is no doubt that labelling can and should be improved and that labels should be geared specifically to Third World conditions. This means the use of local languages and of symbols where possible. The discussion of labelling, though, confirms the conclusion that the availability of the most hazardous pesticides is, in many parts of the Third World, incompatible with local conditions. If these pesticides *are* available it is important that users should be aware, as far as possible, of the conditions necessary for safe use *before* they decide to purchase the product. This is where advertising and promotion come in.

Advertising and Promotion

Advertising and promotion are naturally undertaken by industry to increase the sale of its products, and the promotional message is a very important factor in the decision to buy. If the advertisement says a pesticide is safe and profitable, farmers may buy it on this basis. If this pesticide actually requires specific safety precautions to be taken several things could happen. Farmers, reassured by the advertisement, may not bother to read the label; they may be unable to understand the complex message on the label, but be literate enough to take in the simple message of the advertisement; they may understand the precautions on the label, but be unable to follow them. In the latter case, they may risk poisoning by applying the pesticide regardless, or they may dispose of the pesticide in some way, safe or otherwise. It is likely that the decision to purchase will lead to problems for the farmer. The label instructions come too late to influence that decision.

The promotion in the Third World of a potentially hazardous technology requires a particularly high level of social responsibility. It requires that considerations of safety be given paramount priority even if this appears to be at the expense of sales. The reality, unfortunately, is very different. Promotional efforts often fail to give full and correct information. Yet, these sales efforts have a strong influence on the perceptions of pesticide users and decision-makers. Sri Lanka's Deputy Director of Extension Services says:

> "The companies can spend much on advertising and propaganda which the government cannot afford to combat, and which seems more attractive than the individual contact of the village agricultural extension worker."[17]

"Farmers now know all the names of the pesticides because of intense promotion," says S.R. Jaffarulla, ex-OXFAM field officer in South India.[18] But do they know the hazards?

In the Third World, virtually every available medium is used to persuade people to use pesticides. Respondents to our questionnaires mentioned the following: sales representatives, promotion to government extension workers, billboards, newspaper and journal advertisements, radio and TV, posters, demonstration farms, cinema advertising, and cars and vans with loudspeakers. But in many countries respondents felt that these marketing practices were not consistent with sensible pesticide use and pest control.

92

Extension workers in the Teldeniya area of Sri Lanka explained that, though they are prohibited from recommending particular brands of pesticide, they do make use of posters distributed by the companies, which use trade names. Company representatives also help with demonstrations using samples of their products in cultivators' fields. Both cultivators and extension workers "get the message", and brand names are commonly used by cultivators instead of standard generic names.[19] These extension workers were lively, friendly and dedicated people, who were aware of the strong pressures exerted by company promotional activities both on farmers and on themselves.

In many cases, advertisements fail to mention generic names, so that farmers do not even know the identity of the active ingredient. Farmers are faced with a bewildering variety of formulations. This makes it difficult for them to compare one product with another, and for extension workers to educate farmers about the dangers of particular active ingredients. Surely farmers would be in a better position to use pesticides sensibly and safely if they knew what it was they were using.

Through this armoury of media, the pesticide industry promotes to farmers and extension workers, pesticides which, in some cases, are banned or severely restricted in Western countries. Safety warnings are often missing or inadequate, and in some cases positive claims of safety are made for hazardous products. Advertisements make misleading comparisons of the safety of different products. They make inaccurate or misleading statements about the effects on beneficial insects, fish and animals. They make impossible guarantees of high profits and good harvests, with no mention of other conditions. In all these ways, they present often dangerous chemicals as panaceas for the problems of the Third World farmer. The panacea approach is exemplified by an advertisement by ICI in Central America (advertisement No. 1). The message is that, if you have a pest problem, a chemical is the solution.[20] Other advertisement build on this basic message: even if you have no pest problem, the impression given by some is that you may as well spray anyway, just to be on the safe side. It is sure to increase your profits, say others.

An OXFAM-funded project in Peru, the Comision Coordinadora de Tecnologia Adecuada (Coordinating Commission for Appropriate Technology — CCTA), is carrying out a national enquiry into traditional methods of pest management:

> "We are of the opinion," they say, "that it is wrong to promote
> pest control by means of chemical insecticides alone; first of all
> because these are beyond the reach of the poor peasants, since their
> use also requires the employment of spray equipment and protec-
> tive clothing. Moreover these commercial poisons can cause many
> problems for people who don't know how to read, or understand
> how to apply them."[21]

CCTA summed up the reaction of some farmers in the June 1981 issue of its journal, *Minka:*

> "Advertisements for chemical products present idealised images of
> abundance and trouble-free happiness as a result of applying insecti-
> cides ... But the reality is different. These products no longer
> produce the prodigious results of earlier times. Many campesinos ask
> themselves if they are *bambeados* (bewitched), or if the imports
> are of a lower standard."[22]

In integrated pest management, as we shall see in the next chapter, although pesticides are recognised as important, they are not seen as the automatic first response to the presence of a pest, and prophylactic spraying is discouraged. The safer and more effective management of pests is held back by the dangerous misconceptions which many farmers have about pests and pesticides. This is illustrated, for example, by a recent survey in Nueva Ecija in the Philippines. When faced with an option of using pesticides *or* fertilizers, 78% of farmers chose pesticides, yet none were aware that a leaky sprayer could kill them.[23] Pesticides are seen as safe panaceas partly because they are promoted as such.

Ideally advertising should be used as a form of education in pest management, teaching farmers that not all insects are their enemies, that in the case of a mild pest infestation it may not pay to apply pesticides and that spraying should not as a general rule be undertaken unless a pest is actually present. It should also be used as a form of preventive health education, stressing the dangers involved in pesticide use and the necessity to use pesticides only where appropriate precautions can be taken.

Pesticide advertisements often include *offers* of further information. They may also include disclaimers to the effect that no responsibility will be accepted by the advertiser for any damage or injury resulting from the use of the product. Thirdly, there may be an exhortation to read the label when the product has been purchased. All these statements are unlikely to convey an effective warning to the user that the product is hazardous and that certain precautions will be necessary to ensure safety.

The constructive use of advertising as a bearer of safety information and for the promotion of sensible and integrated pest management has great potential for improving farmers' understanding and so helping to overcome the problems which result from pesticide misuse. It is evident that some regulation is required to ensure such a high standard of responsibility in promotional practices.

There are very few controls on advertising and promotion, let alone specific controls which deal with the special problems of promoting pesticides. Those which do exist are poorly enforced and insufficiently specific. The International Chamber of Commerce (ICC), for example, publishes an international code of practice.[24] This states the basic principle that:

"All advertising should be legal, decent, honest and truthful. Every advertisement should be prepared with a due sense of social responsibility."[25]

The ICC Code recognises that small print in advertisements cannot provide escape from these obligations:

"Advertisements should be judged," it says, "by their likely impact on the consumer, bearing in mind that the consumer is usually motivated by the impression gained from a brief scanning of the advertisement."[26]

Other relevant sections from the ICC Code include:

"*Article 2*: Advertisements should be so framed as not to abuse the trust of the consumer or exploit his lack of experience or knowledge."[27]

94

"Article 12: Advertisements should not without reason, justifiable on educational or social grounds, contain any visual presentation or any description of dangerous practices or of situations which show a disregard for safety..."[28]

The Code contains further special provisions for certain advertising practices and particular goods and services. For example:

"A.1. Guarantees ... Advertisements may contain the word guarantee ... or words having the same meaning only if the full terms of the guarantee as well as the remedial action open to the purchaser are clearly set out in the advertisements, or are available to the purchaser in writing at the point of sale, or with the goods ..."[29]

"B.9. Dangerous products: Advertisements for products which are potentially poisonous or flammable or otherwise dangerous but which may not be readily recognised as such by consumers should indicate the potential danger of such products."[30]

Despite the vague generality of the ICC Code, it is useful as a yardstick against which to measure pesticide advertising in the Third World. As we shall see, the Code appears to be frequently infringed.

Various national governments have specific legislation on pesticide advertising and this too can be used as a yardstick. In Malaysia, for example, the Pesticides Board have decided to prohibit the use of certain statements in advertising. The rules are due to come into full force from January 1982.[31] They are very basic rules, which companies should surely apply regardless of legislation. The prohibited statements are as follows:

1 Claims as to the safety of the pesticide or its ingredients, including statements such as "safe", "non-poisonous", "non-injurious", "harmless", or "non-toxic to humans and pets", with or without such a qualifying phrase as "when used as directed".

2 Comparative statements on the safety of the product, eg "among the least toxic chemicals known".

3 A false or misleading statement concerning the effectiveness of the product as a pesticide.

4 A false or misleading comparison with other pesticides.

5 The words "odourless", "sweet-smelling", "fragrant" or any other similar word.[32]

Following discussions with OXFAM, the British Agrochemicals Association have expressed agreement that the word "safe" should not be used in pesticide advertising.[33] This is perhaps the most essential, and simple, rule. Far higher standards are needed, yet even this rule is not universally adhered to.

Bearing in mind the yardsticks of the ICC Code and the new Malaysian legislation, let us look at some of the promotional material which we have collected during 1980 and 1981. The reader will be able to identify the shortcomings of this material in the light of the guidelines listed. We shall therefore give only brief commentaries on the advertisements illustrated. These fall into four broad categories, although there is considerable overlap.

Restricted Products

First, there are those advertisements which promote products that are widely restricted, especially in Europe and America, yet which give no indication of hazards to man or the environment. In one case the advertisement even stresses the safety of such a product.

Chlordane (advertisement No. 2), promoted by Velsicol in Malaysia, is banned in the EEC.[34] It is classified by WHO as "moderately hazardous". In the US, most uses were cancelled with effect from 31 December 1980.[35] The only uses permitted are ground insertion against termites and dipping of roots or tops of non-food crops. Chlordane is very persistent in the environment. In this advertisement, chlordane was described as "safe" and on the picture of the can it says: "Comparatively, it is the safest insecticide for ... control of insects, ants ... termites". The next page of the advertisement (not reproduced here) recommended application to rice foliage against grasshoppers, and various applications against ants and cutworms on fruits and vegetables. On the third page there is a comparison of chlordane with other chemicals in terms of acute oral toxicity. These other chemicals include heptachlor, which is closely related to chlordane and is also banned in Europe and the US for almost all uses, as are the pair of chemicals aldrin and dieldrin. Endrin is also severely restricted in Europe and the US and is, in any case, banned in Malaysia.[36] Both dieldrin and parathion, also included in this comparison, are classified by WHO in class 1A (extremely hazardous). Comparison with this group of chemicals is certainly no guarantee of safety. In any case, the oral LD_{50} figure given for technical chlordane in the WHO/FAO data sheet[37] is between 335 mg/kg (male rats) and 430 mg/kg (female rats). The data sheet also states that man is one of the most susceptible species, with an approximate LD_{50} of 100 mg/kg. When opening the container and mixing chlordane, the data sheet recommends the wearing of boots, overalls, gloves and a respirator.

In response to OXFAM's enquiries, Velsicol have agreed that it is improper to label any pesticide absolutely 'safe'. They are currently checking on advertising copy for all their international products.[38]

Heptachlor (advertisement No. 3) has also been promoted by Velsicol. In this advertisement from Central America (July 1980) it was recommended for corn, sorghum, potatoes, rice and other crops. Heptachlor is banned in Europe and the US for almost all uses, due to the persistence of its breakdown products and the resulting hazard to the environment. It is also moderately toxic. The advertisement urges the consumer to read the label, but gives no further indication of danger. Velsicol are still using this advertisement. They say that:

> "There are no misleading statements in the ad copy and we find this ad completely acceptable."[39]

Another advertisement from Malaysia is for 2,4,5-T marketed by ICI (advertisement No. 4). The doubts about 2,4,5-T are now well known in Britain, and it is banned for most uses in the US, Sweden, Norway, Holland and Italy.[40] The WHO/FAO data sheet for 2,4,5-T says that "protective clothing should be provided for those handling the compound" and that "pregnant women are advised not to enter sprayed areas."[41] The only caution given in the advertisement is against allowing drift on to other plants. No ordinary consumer reading this advertisement would have the slightest idea that there could be any risk involved in the use of this chemical. Yet ICI "did not agree that this advertisement could be improved by the inclusion of some indication of potential hazard". ICI did agree that purchasers require all potential hazard information before they decide to purchase, but felt that the label would serve this purpose.[42]

Safety

These are particular problem pesticides, but, moving on to the second category of questionable advertising, it is important that *no* pesticides should be described as safe. US expert Virgil Freed says that,

> "any chemical in sufficient concentration may be toxic. This is a cardinal principle ... In categorising some chemicals as being less toxic than others, we tend to forget that an excessive dose of even so-called safe chemicals can be injurious".[43]

Minimum safety precautions should be followed when dealing with *any* pesticide. In particular, people using any pesticide should wear at least some footwear, long trousers, a long-sleeved shirt and a hat.[44] Yet, ICI have advertised Agrocide, a formulation of gamma BHC (advertisement No. 5), in Malaysia with pictures of a sprayman with bare feet, short trousers and a short-sleeved shirt. Gamma BHC is not an especially dangerous pesticide — it is classified by WHO as moderately hazardous. Yet for liquid formulations over 5% and solids over 20%, the WHO/FAO data sheet for lindane (BHC containing at least 99% gamma isomer) recommends protective clothing for those handling the concentrate.[45] The advertisement could also encourage farmers to believe that *any* pesticide can be applied with such an absence of precautions. We approached ICI about this advertisement. They agreed that this advertisement is "inappropriate" and "representations have been made to ICI Malaysia and the advertisement is being discontinued."[46]

Dow's chemical Dursban (advertisement No. 6) has been advertised in Malaysia with the words: "The + Means Safety". Dow point out that this advertisement is no longer in use, but admit that "perhaps it would have been appropriate to utilize the negative side and say Dursban presented less hazard".[47] With their letter, Dow enclosed the current Malaysian label for Dursban. This label makes no mention of the protective clothing recommended by WHO[48] nor of any hazard to bees and fish.

Cynamid's Cythion (malathion) has been advertised in India (advertisement No. 7) as "the safe insecticide" which enables you to "be sure of a bumper coffee crop".

In Central America in July 1980 Boots advertised their product Mitac (amitraz) (advertisement No. 8) for use in integrated control programmes, boasting of its "high degree of security for ... the environment". In Britain it has been recommended that amitraz be covered by the Health and Safety Regulations, requiring the use of protective clothing. The UK recommendations stress that it is harmful to fish: "do not contaminate ponds, waterways and ditches". It is also recommended that it be covered by the Poisons Rules. The advertisement contains no details of any potential danger to man or to the environment. Concerning the product's safety to the environment, FBC Ltd (the UK company formed by a merger of the agrochemical divisions of Fisons and Boots) "accepted that there is an inconsistency" and agreed to investigate the matter further.[49]

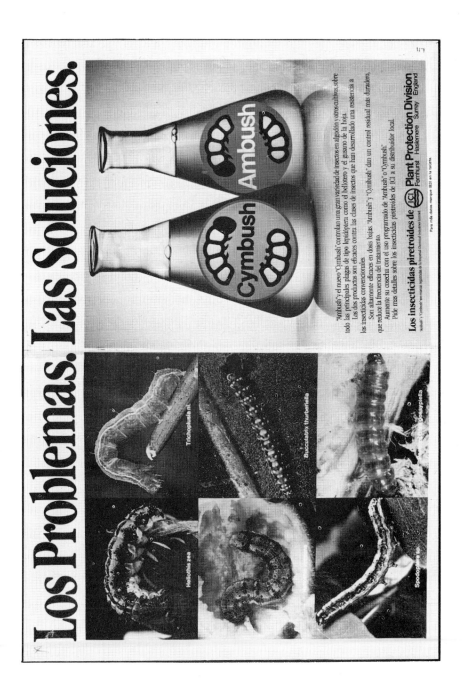

Advertisement No. 1

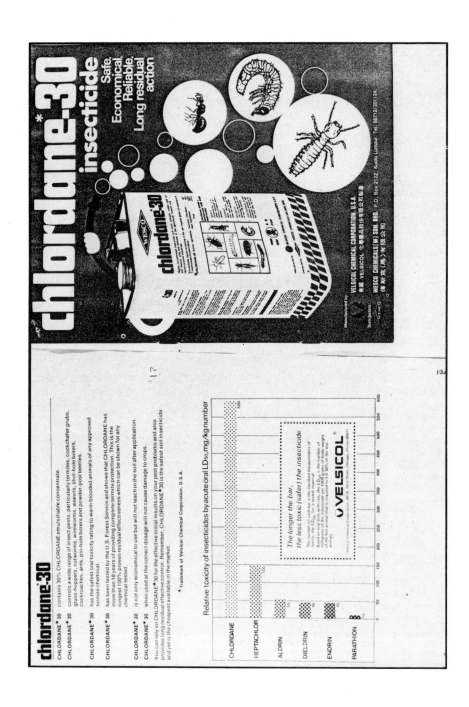

Advertisement No. 3

2, 4, 5-T

2, 4, 5-T Concentrated (unformulated) Butyl Ester 'Cock's Head' Brand.

Acid equivalent 10 lb. per gallon. A liquid formulation which can be used against vigorous broad-leaved weeds, particularly those types not susceptible to 2, 4-D.

A 1% solution in diesel oil is generally recommended. For use with low volume spraying equipment, work on the basis of 2½ to 3 pints of the concentrated 2, 4, 5-T per acre.

For use as a tree-killer, dilute 1 part with 19 parts of diesel oil. Apply the solution using a brush or a piece of hessian cloth by painting or rubbing a 6-9 inch band of the solution on to the stem at a height of 15 inches from the ground. If a second application is necessary for the "hard-to-kill' woody trees, repeat the operation below the 15-inch mark.

'TRIFEN' — 2,4,5-T Miscible Liquid

Acid equivalent 5 lb. per gallon. This is a liquid formulation miscible with water or oil recommended for use in water at rates of 5 to 6 pints per 80 to 100 gallons of water per acre, against Straits Rhodedendron *(Melastoma malabathricum)* and other shrubby growths.

CAUTION

Never allow drift from the spray of hormone-type weedkillers to come into contact with leaves of valuable trees or plants as they are likely to be defoliated or even killed.

CONDITIONS OF SUPPLY

All goods supplied by us are of high grade and we believe them to be suitable, but (as we cannot exercise control over their mixing or use) all conditions and warranties, statutory or otherwise, as to the quality or fitness for any purpose of our goods are excluded, and no responsibility will be accepted by us for any damage or injury whatsoever arising from their storage, handling, application or use.

Advertisement No. 4

2,4,5-T & 'TRIFEN'

HERBICIDE

 I.C.I. AGRICULTURE (MALAYSIA) SDN. BERHAD

Advertisement No. 6

DECEMBER 1979

Advertisement No. 7

 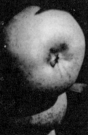  
Advertisement No. 8

106

Bidrin 24
destroys insects before they destroy your orchids

Bidrin 24 is an organophosphorous insecticide that protects your orchids in a different way. Unlike other insecticides, which stay on the plant and give superficial protection, Bidrin 24 is absorbed into the plant tissue and remains there for 3 to 4 weeks. And because it is in the plant, it is completely unaffected by the weather.

This way, your orchids get long lasting protection against all kinds of sucking, biting and chewing insects.

For supplies contact any Tiram Kimia dealer. On other pests control contact Tiram Kimia office nearest to you.

TIRAM KIMIA SDN. BHD.,
P.O. BOX 1027,
KUALA LUMPUR.
TEL: 940055

Shell Chemicals

TIRAM KIMIA SDN. BHD.

Señores Agricultores
TAMARON 600

es un INSECTICIDA y ACARICIDA con efecto de contacto y digestión, de penetración al follaje y a toda materia orgánica viva, con efecto sistémico y de una residualidad de 8 a 14 días, dependiendo ésto de la temperatura y humedad ambiental.

Controla entre otros: gusanos (larvas y orugas) insectos chupadores (moscas blancas pulgones, chicharritas), insectos minadores y ácaros resistentes.

TAMARON 600

es un CAMPEON entre los productos BAYER para proteger toda clase de cultivos en tierra templada y tierra fría y, en las plantaciones de algodón tiene fama indiscutida garantizando buenas cosechas.

Servicio Técnico **Bayer** (BAYER)

1a. Avenida 8-01, Zona 10. Tels.: 314959

REVOLUCION VERDE—7

Advertisement No. 10

Advertisement No. 11

109

132

Sumitomo Chemical. Dreaming and Doing.

While these little sidewalk artists are on their knees, dreaming and doing...we're at our drawing boards, dreaming and doing, too. It's essentially the same dream: a cleaner, prettier, safer world. But in the doing, that's where "the Sumitomo difference" comes in.

Some of our more recent advances in pesticides, for instance, have made giant

contributions to the world these children will inherit soon. Several of our new insecticides, Sumicidin* for cotton infestation and Sumisclex* (Sumilex*) to combat vineyard fungi, have had tremendous impact on agriculture. And the recent global outbreak of locusts was brought under control by the help of Sumithion*(fenitrothion).

The world's continuing food supply: it's all part of our dream. And we're working hard to see that mankind's dream for a better world tomorrow comes true. With industrial chemicals, fertilizers, plastics, synthetic rubber, dyestuffs, fine chemicals, pesticides and pharmaceuticals... all with "the Sumitomo difference."

❖ SUMITOMO CHEMICAL CO., LTD.
Osaka. Japan

❖ SUMITOMO CORPORATION
Osaka. Japan

Advertisement No. 12

110

PORQUE EL EDEN TAMBIEN
TENIA SUS PARASITOS

Advertisement No. 13

111

112

113

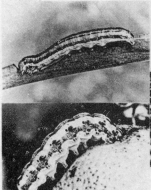

Advertisement No. 15

Advertisement No. 16

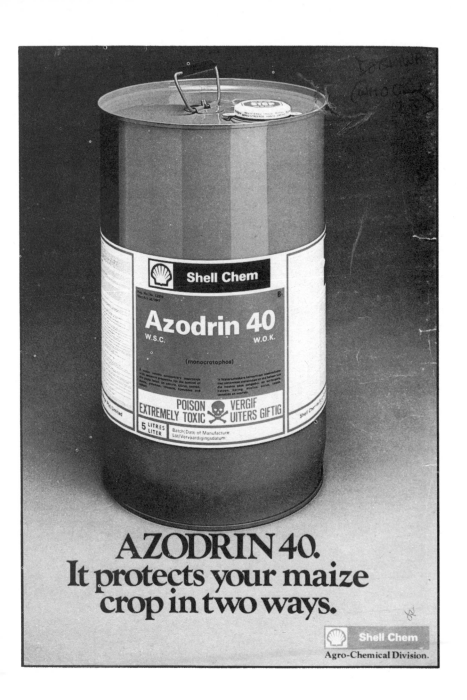

AZODRIN 40.
It protects your maize crop in two ways.

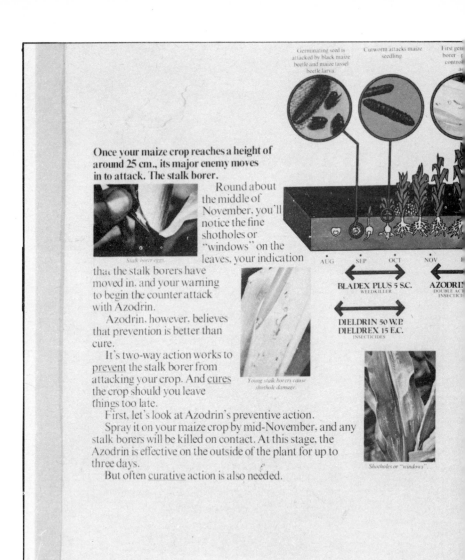

Once your maize crop reaches a height of around 25 cm., its major enemy moves in to attack. The stalk borer.

Round about the middle of November, you'll notice the fine shotholes or "windows" on the leaves, your indication that the stalk borers have moved in, and your warning to begin the counter attack with Azodrin.

Azodrin, however, believes that prevention is better than cure.

It's two-way action works to prevent the stalk borer from attacking your crop. And cures the crop should you leave things too late.

First, let's look at Azodrin's preventive action.

Spray it on your maize crop by mid-November, and any stalk borers will be killed on contact. At this stage, the Azodrin is effective on the outside of the plant for up to three days.

But often curative action is also needed.

Germinating seed is attacked by black maize beetle and maize tassel beetle larva.

Cutworm attacks maize seedling.

Stalk borer eggs.

Young stalk borers cause shothole damage.

Shotholes or "windows".

BLADEX PLUS 5 S.C.
WEEDKILLER

AZODRIN
DOUBLE ACTION
INSECTICIDE

DIELDRIN 50 W.P.
DIELDREX 15 E.C.
INSECTICIDES

AUG   SEP   OCT   NOV

種植禾稻的大改革

種植前採用「加威素」除草劑——良好成長，容易清除稻田。
採用「加威素」能迅速清除雜草。
縮短土地準備工作時間。
節省時間及準備一切土地耕前種前的工作。
「加威素」能使你在若干土地中省却耕耘的麻煩。
「加威素」不含毒素不傷害土壤。

「加威素」—用途廣泛的除草劑

'GRAMOXON

'GRAM

① 「加威素」一液體安士及「愛克素四」半液體安士滲以每一加侖的清水。

Mix 1 fluid ounce of 'Gramoxone' and ½ fluid ounce of 'Agroxone' 4 to every gallon of clean water used.

② 徹底地噴射稻田的每一角落，以四十加侖藥液噴射一依吉地（三十加侖噴射 — relong）。

Spray the padi fields thoroughly. Apply 40 gallons of spray to each acre (30 gallons per relong).

③ 噴射後

3–5 d into the field

⑥ 種植後十天，施用 BHC 粒以預防蛀莖虫侵害。

10 days after planting apply BHC Granules to prevent stem borer attack.

⑦ 種植後二十天，噴射「愛克素四」以消滅闊葉，蘆葦草，然後如果是短稻類(Bahagia 與 Ria)則施放尿素肥料。

20 days after planting spray the field with 'Agroxone' 4 to kill broad-leafed weeds and sedges. After that use urea fertilizer if the padi are short straw varieties (Bahagia and Ria).

⑧ 種植後四

40 d Granules ag

THE REVOLUTION IN PADI PLANTING.

USE 'GRAMOXONE' TO KILL WEEDS BEFORE PLANTING —
GROW BETTER CLEANER PADI MORE EASILY.

With 'GRAMOXONE' you can kill weeds quickly and save weeks
in preparing land. Greatly reduce time and work involved in
preparing land for planting.

'Gramoxone' can eliminate the need for all cultivation in some
areas.

'Gramoxone' does not poison the soil.

'GRAMOXONE' THE VERSATILE WEEDKILLER

ONE'
PP910

稻田徹底浸水後較好枯死的雜
草使埋入土壤內，然後好平土壤及
施放稻田精肥料 • Baja Padi Mewah.
吉蘭丹州。則施放 Baja Padi Ma'amor.

After flooding the rice field
moderately, cultivate the soil so that the
dead weeds are buried. Make the rice field
even and broadcast Baja Padi Mewah. In
Kelantan, use Baja Padi Ma'amor.

浸稻田。

let the water

将稻苗移植稻田上。

Transplant the padi seedlings into the field.

種植後六十天，為短稻類施放
第二次的尿素肥料，如果是長稻類
(Malinja 與 Mahsuri) 則在此時施放第
一次尿素肥料的好時候。吉蘭丹州
則自六至八個星期內，施放第二次
的 Paja Padi Ma'amor.

60 days after planting use urea
fertilizer for the second time for padi of
short straw varieties. For long straw
varieties (Malinja and Mahsuri), this is the
only time when urea is used. In Kelantan,
between 6 to 8 weeks, use Baja Padi
Ma'amor for the second time.

BHC 粒。

apply BHC

採用「愛克强」或「賽文」殺虫
剤，消滅食葉昆虫。

Control leaf eating insects with
'Agrothion' or 'Sevin' insecticide.

Back in Malaysia Shell advertised Bidrin 24 (dicrotophos) (advertisement No. 9). Dicrotophos is in WHO Class 1B, "highly hazardous". The advertisement gives no hint of danger beyond the small skull and crossbones which appears on the bottle. In Guatemala Bayer advertised Tamaron (methamidophos) (advertisement No. 10). This, too, is in WHO Class 1B and the advertisement mentions no hazards. Guatemalan regulations specify that advertisements must give "all technical data relating to [the product's] qualities, and the safety measures relating to its use".[50] Bayer claim to "abide strictly by the laws of recipient countries", but argue that "it is not customary anywhere in the world to mention the poison classification of a product in newspaper advertisements".[51]

In the Central American magazine, *Agricultura de las Americas,* July 1980, the Japanese company Sumitomo promoted Sumithion (fenitrothion) (advertisement No. 11) as "a strong, safe insecticide" having "low toxicity for humans and natural life". UK recommendations for fenitrothion say that operators should "wear rubber gloves and a face-shield when handling the concentrate". It is classified by WHO as "moderately hazardous". In Britain the label must state "Harmful to livestock .... harmful to game, wild birds and animals ... harmful to bees ... harmful to fish".

Yet, in Britain, in *South,* a Third World magazine, Sumitomo advertise themselves as "working hard to see that mankind's dream for a better world tomorrow comes true" (advertisement No. 12).[52]

We approached Sumitomo by letter to express concern about the use of the word "safe" in their Sumithion advertisement. They replied that one of their distributors had already pointed out that this was "not proper". They added: "We have requested our advertisement agent in Japan to modify the wording accordingly." After describing their advertising procedures, the Sumitomo representative concluded:

> "We admit that our way is not sophisticated at all at this moment,
> but we will try to improve in the future."[53]

Two months later Sumitomo notified OXFAM that the word 'Seguro' (safe) in the advertisement had been replaced by the words 'poco venenoso' (little poisonous).[54] Whilst this is certainly a welcome improvement, the advertisement still gives insufficient information regarding the potential hazard of the product and the necessary safety precautions.

The Italian Company Montedison (advertisement No. 13), have advertised their products in Central America with the words "maximum safety for man and the environment". This, they say, is one of the "requirements Montedison has followed in its research". In addition, the advertisement states that Rogor (dimethoate) has "low toxicity". In fact, dimethoate is classified by WHO as "moderately hazardous". In Britain, rubber gloves and a face-shield are recommended when handling the concentrate and the label says it is harmful to livestock, game, wild birds, animals, bees and fish. The WHO/FAO data sheet on dimethoate includes a minimum cautionary statement for dimethoate labels. This states: "It is poisonous if swallowed. It may be absorbed through the skin or inhaled...wear protective gloves, clean protective clothing and a dust mask."[55] Montedison point out that this advertisement appeared in a magazine aimed at "skilled agricultural technicians and operators". In response to our enquiry, Montedison said that "as far as Rogor dimethoate is concerned the great claim to non-toxicity is not in our opinion unwarranted". Concerning their general advertising policy Montedison said, "we believe we are rather conservative in our claims for our products in our advertising material".[56]

In India Fisons and their Indian associate Rallis advertised Furadan (carbofuran) granules (a product of the US-based FMC Corporation) (advertisement No. 14) with the words "Furadan 3G granules are safe to handle". Following discussions with OXFAM, FBC have agreed to approach Rallis in India, through Fisons, concerning this advertisement. FBC agree that the word 'safe' should not be used.[57] FMC have also taken up this matter with Rallis.[58]

Guarantees

This advertisement also takes us into the third are of questionable advertising -- the promotion of the idea that a pesticide guarantees or virtually guarantees higher yields and profits. In reality, of course, yield and profits depend on many factors: prices of inputs and crops, weather conditions, soil fertility and labour input are some of these. Pesticides are unlikely to provide significant yield increases if there is no significant pest attack and even then they may not increase profits especially for the small farmer growing a low value crop.

Dow in Guatemala have gone even further, stating that Lorsban (chlorpyrifos) *"guarantees* a good harvest" (our emphasis). No safety instructions are included in the advertisement (No. 15). Union Carbide have claimed in Malaysia that Temik (aldicarb) "increases profits fast" (advertisement No. 16).

Agricultural Practices

Finally, advertisements promote pest control practices which are not the most consistent with long-term safety and efficacy. In particular, the practice of calendar spraying (spraying at certain times of year or of the crop cycle) wastes pesticide and increases selection pressure for resistance, by spraying even when no pest is present. An OECD report says,

> "There is evidence that, in following such a pattern without
> reference to the real pest situation, an unnecessarily heavy load of
> chemicals is applied, entailing toxicological hazards, adverse effects
> on the agroecosystem and a disruption of natural enemies. Further-
> more, applications of pesticides beyond the effective need entails
> considerable extra cost which may render a crop uneconomic.
> This is particularly so when the repeated spraying favours the
> development of resistant pest species, bringing about a situation
> in which the frequency of applications and dosage has to be
> constantly increased. There are examples where certain crops
> have had to be abandoned because of such circumstances."[59]

Wherever pesticides can be applied on the basis of the observed presence of pest populations, this is preferable to the calendar approach. It would therefore be helpful if advertisements did more to emphasise the value of application based on pest 'thresholds'.

Despite this Shell, in Botswana, have promoted calendar spraying of dieldrin and azodrin (monocrotophos) (advertisement No. 17). Shell, while agreeing that calendar spraying could lead to unnecessary pesticide use, felt that in this particular case thresholds would be difficult to operate. They therefore prefer to continue with the existing format of the advertisement.[60] This advertisement does not recommend spraying solely by the calendar, since thresholds related to the degree of pest infestation are given at the bottom right. Nevertheless, the layout of the advertisement emphasises the calendar approach. In addition, these chemicals are classified by WHO as "extremely hazardous" and "highly hazardous" respectively.

ICI, in Malaysia, have promoted the application of BHC granules on a calendar basis (advertisement No. 18). ICI have claimed that this use of BHC granules is acceptable on the grounds that once pest damage is visible, it is too late for effective treatment of stem borer.[61] We approached the Malaysian Agricultural Research and Development Institute (MARDI) concerning the prophylactic use of BHC granules against stem borer. Calendar application *was* recommended, says Dr. Heong of MARDI, but now, "We have gone away from the calendar spray recommendation of the past to the use of thresholds".[62] ICI now inform us that the leaflet concerned "is no longer current".[63]

Safe and effective use of pesticides in the Third World is not likely to be achieved until promotional practices are improved. Extension services are constantly battling against the attitudes instilled by advertising. "Control by firms on advertising and promotion would help", says Sri Lanka's Deputy Director of Extension Services, Mr Percy Abeywardena.[64]

Dr. Lucas Brader, FAO's Head of Plant Protection Service says:

"IPM is less costly than chemical pest control, so on paper economic barriers should not exist. However, one has to consider the fact that the pesticide industry has a very strongly organised sales promotion system. Industry is not against IPM, as it constitutes a system to make the best use of pesticides. But at the same time company salesmen wish to boost their sales. In situtations such as cotton growing, where IPM would reduce the number of pesticide applications, one may expect conflict."[65]

* * * * * * *

In view of the special problems involved in the use of pesticides in the Third World, it is essential that labelling and promotional practices are subject to international controls. A code of practice should be drawn up by WHO and FAO and perhaps UNEP. The code should include provisions to prevent all the kinds of inadequate, inappropriate or misleading labelling and promotion dealt with in this chapter. Such a code should be as strong and binding as possible and enforcement ensured by the active involvement of all interested agencies in the monitoring process. The British Agrochemicals Association are in favour of an international code on pesticide advertising. It requires only that a member government of the UN raise the suggestion officially and negotiations can begin.

It is also important that the greatest efforts be made by those monitoring the code to ensure that enforcement extends to local formulators and distributors operating within Third World countries, as well as to the international companies.

In short, the international community must do all in its power to ensure that promotional activities encourage safety and sensible pest management, rather than just sell a brand of chemical. This is one of the most important steps which can be taken to safeguard the lives and livelihoods of Third World farmers and farmworkers against the problems of pesticide use. "Safety before sales" should be the universal motto of the international community and the pesticide industry.

 # Integrated Pest Management and the Poor Farmer

INTEGRATED PEST MANAGEMENT AND THE POOR FARMER

T he farmers of the Third World and their governments are faced with a choice. This choice is not between pesticides and no pesticides. They can choose a hazardous and potentially ineffective or counterproductive dependence on a pest management strategy based solely on the uncontrolled application of chemicals. Or they can choose instead to opt for a pest management strategy which is both safer and more effective. Such a strategy would incorporate farmers' traditional practices instead of replacing them. It would apply only technologies which could be safely used under Third World conditions. It would reduce dependence on imported inputs and would be geared to the needs of small farmers and landless labourers. Despite the attraction and promotion of the chemical strategy, many people, including some of the farmers themselves, are beginning to realise that a change is needed. The farmers should be actively involved in this change not simply its passive recipients. There are no panaceas, but the search is on for a better way.

What does such an alternative strategy look like? The task is to maximise the use of safe, cheap and simple pest management techniques, including those tradition-ally used by Third World farmers, and to integrate these with the use of the safest possible chemical pesticides, where necessary, into a strategy which could deal with pest problems as a part of a system — including people, crops, beneficial insects, fish and livestock, as well as pests and chemicals. Such an ecological approach constitutes the best use of pesticides. It is also the basis of the idea of integrated pest management (IPM).

Integrated Pest Management

IPM attempts to apply more than a single pest management technique in such a way that the different methods complement each other. The need for such an approach is demonstrated by the failure of the single-component chemical strategy:

> "The empirical and unilateral use of chemicals to attempt to hammer pests into submission by repeated costly blows is... increasingly failing to provide a solution," says entomologist Professor Paul DeBach. "A rapid and drastic change is necessary in order to achieve control of pests in an ecologically and economically satisfactory manner."[1]

Robert Richter

The failure of single-component pest control is particularly crucial for small farmers in the Third World. A recent OECD report stated:

"The small farmer producing low-value (per unit) crops, frequently under adverse climatic conditions, cannot solve pest problems economically by chemical control alone... Considering the many inconveniences which result from essentially chemical crop protection systems, other more ecologically oriented systems have to be sought."[2]

The IPM concept represents the ideal of an ecological approach. It is a concept which is much talked about and often defined. It is also known as Integrated Pest Control (IPC) — the terms are interchangeable. We will here quote only one definition of IPM since this is sufficient for a general understanding of the concept. The more important discussion concerns the implementation of IPM in the Third World and specifically by the small farmer. The definition we have chosen is from Professor Ray F. Smith and J.L. Apple. Professor Smith is one of the world's foremost proponents of IPM and has specialised in its application in the Third World:

"Integrated pest control is a broad ecological approach to pest control, utilizing a variety of control technologies compatibly in a single pest management system. In integrated pest control, stress is placed on the importance of realistic economic injury levels which are used to determine the need for control actions. At the same time, all possible is done to protect and preserve naturally occurring biotic mortality agents such as parasites, predators and pathogens. When artificial controls are needed, for example chemical pesticide applications, they are employed in as selective a manner as possible and only when their use is economically and ecologically justified. The ultimate objective of the integrated pest control system is to produce the optimum crop yield of high quality at minimum cost, taking into consideration the ecological and sociological constraints in that particular agroecosystem and the long-term preservation of the environment. This is the ideal of integrated control toward which we should strive."[3]

IPM can draw upon a number of different pest management methods. These include the careful and selective use of pesticides as well as biological and cultural controls, physical controls, the use of pest resistant plant varieties and a number of other techniques. Let us look at these in turn.

Biological Control

Biological control makes use of pests' natural enemies to keep their population down. This means farming in such a way as to make the most of existing natural enemies, for example by using pesticides as carefully and selectively as possible. Classical biological control entails introducing an enemy of a pest for the purpose of controlling that pest. Biological control provides no immediate and certain results, but at its best is very economical and efficient. The aim is to establish a once-for-all self-regulatory system in which natural enemies keep the pest below a damaging level.

In some cases, natural enemies can be mass-produced by groups of farmers. Such production is extensively used at village level in China, for example.[4] The Commonwealth Institute for Biological Control has been working on both the theory and the practice of biological control since 1927. They estimate that savings of over £3 million a year have been made against an annual expenditure of £350,000.[5] One project for biological control of a coconut pest in Sri Lanka is saving over £1 million a year from a total expenditure of £30,000.[6]

DeBach has found that the importation of biological control organisms has resulted in permanent control (complete, substantial or partial) of at least 120 species of pest insects. But only 223 species have been subjected to this method out of some 5,000 recorded insect pests. Financial returns from reduced chemical costs and lessened crop damage have been estimated at about 30 to 1. Also, it seems that the success rate has been greater in tropical areas, which are especially favourable to the activity of natural enemies.[7]

It should not be forgotten though, that rigorous safety evaluations are necessary for biological control agents before their introduction. As in the case of pesticides the potential indirect effects need to be taken into account in assessing the return on investments.

Cultural and Physical Control

Cultural controls are usually the most economical pest control methods and are widely applicable. They include the destruction of crop residues (stubble etc) after harvest, fallow periods, crop rotation and the careful timing of planting, weeding and harvesting. Many such techniques are part of the traditional knowledge of Third World farmers and need to be preserved and take their place in sensible pest management systems. Other cultural methods are more innovative, such as the use of trap crops. These are small areas of crops which are planted in order to attract pests. This crop is then destroyed or sprayed, thus protecting the main crop from attack.

Cultural controls, such as correct timing of planting, are likely to be more effective if practised in a co-ordinated fashion by many farmers in a given area. This is also true of other aspects of IPM.

Physical and mechanical controls involve the direct destruction or reduction of pests such as hand-weeding, sticky bands round tree trunks, fences, or even the common fly swatter. More sophisticated methods include the use of light to trap night-flying insects.

Resistant Plant Varieties and Other Methods

The use of plant varieties resistant to attack has been practised for many decades. The plant's ability to resist attack is generally due to its production of substances disliked by the pest, or to its physical character (such as hairy leaves), or to its ability to recover well from attack. From the farmer's viewpoint, such varieties represent a very attractive method of pest control. Traditional varieties are often fairly pest-resistant, in contrast to many of the new Green Revolution hybrids. Recently, new varieties have been successfully bred for pest resistance, although this resistance may break down as the pest adapts to its new environment.

Other pest management techniques include the release of large numbers of sterile male insects in order to reduce breeding. This method requires the ability to breed and sterilise large numbers of insects and does not appear to be applicable at the small farmer level, at least in the short-term.[8] Another method involves the use of chemicals to alter insects' behaviour. Pheremones, for example, include synthetic sex-attractants which can be used to disrupt mating or to lure insects into traps.

Economic Damage Thresholds and Monitoring

A number of the methods described can be used together in IPM programmes with the objective of keeping pest populations below the "economic damage, or injury, threshold". This is the level of infestation below which the cost of control measures is greater than the value of crops lost. The aim is not to eradicate the pest, but to keep its population within these tolerable bounds. This implies the need for farmers to know the level of pest infestation in their fields. This is achieved by 'scouting' or 'monitoring', which essentially entails keeping a regular eye on the pests, and if possible on the beneficial organisms too. At the simplest level this allows a farmer to avoid the expense of spraying when pests are not present in significant numbers. The avoidance of such 'prophylactic' or 'calendar' spraying saves money and reduces the amount of pesticide use, and therefore the hazards associated with such use. At the most sophisticated level, completely unsuitable for the small Third World farmer, the information gained from monitoring can be fed into a computer together with crop values and treatment costs in order to produce predictions about the necessity of pesticide application.

Pesticides in IPM

IPM, then, does not mean the complete abandonment of pesticides, although it will cut out any excessive or unnecessary pesticide use. In fact, the use of pesticides in IPM is the best use of pesticides. This does not, though, mean that their hazards can be forgotten. A good IPM programme will also include measures to minimize the hazards of the pesticides which are used. The correct use of pesticides in IPM recognises and stresses the importance of correct timing of application in the correct dosage. The pesticide used should be as safe and selective as possible.

Selective pesticides are those which affect the target pest with minimum adverse effects on other organisms. These ideal chemicals are not generally available and, although some research has been carried out, a chemical useful for only one pest would have a relatively small market and so be unlikely to repay its development costs. Nevertheless, such chemicals are greatly preferable and further research on their development should be encouraged. This could necessitate greater involvement of governmental agencies in pesticides research.

In the meantime, existing chemicals must be used as selectively as possible. Chemicals can be used more selectively by applying them at the time, and in the dosage, which minimises their effect on natural enemies; by applying the most appropriate formulations, and by using the best application equipment. Some equipment, for example, applies pesticides at 'ultra low volume' (ULV) or in droplets of controlled sizes. These techniques can save substantially on the total quantity of active ingredient applied. They can also do away with the necessity to mix and dilute the chemical before spraying — it is supplied in a bottle for direct attachment to the sprayer. This is especially beneficial from a safety viewpoint since opening containers and mixing ingredients are perhaps the most hazardous operations for the pesticide user. Battery-operated ULV sprayers suitable for use by small farmers have been developed.

A further refinement is the electrostatic sprayer which electrically charges the pesticide droplets so that they are attracted to the plant. This can reduce the wastage which normally occurs when a large proportion of the chemical misses the plant altogether.

Essentially the idea is to spray only when absolutely necessary, and then to use as little pesticide as possible as safely as possible. This means that pesticide management is an essential part of pest management. Professor Smith and others have stressed this fact:

> "Pesticide management is seen as an integral component of pest and vector management; it is our belief that the ultimate goals of improved food production and the control of vector borne diseases will only be achieved through the integrated approaches to pest management... Safe pesticide management is therefore an essential component and possibly a prerequisite of integrated pest control."[9]

Pesticide management includes all aspects of the safe, efficient and economic use and handling of pesticides. In order to achieve this, it is necessary to involve both the agricultural and medical disciplines. Such an 'agromedical' approach means involving agricultural extension workers in a wider concept of community care, including preventive health. In terms of pesticides, community health practitioners and agricultural extension workers should be involved together in teaching people about the safe use of pesticides and in recognising and helping to treat cases of pesticide poisoning. In the rural areas of the Third World health and agriculture are so closely linked that the agromedical idea is completely logical.

There is now widespread acceptance in all quarters that IPM is the best pest control strategy and, indeed, many feel it to be the only strategy which can help us to achieve the long-term goals of increased food production and the control of vector-borne diseases. Statements in support of IPM have come from USAID, FAO, OECD and many experts in the West and in the Third World, including the chemical industry:

> "Industry ... does not hestiate to record its commitment to the general philosophy of integrated control"[10]

said a booklet of the Co-Operative Programme of Agro-Allied Industries with FAO as long ago as 1972. And indeed the industry has contributed to the development of IPM through the development of new application and formulation techniques and novel chemical approaches to pest management.

But expressions of support, from whatever quarter, are not enough. Even some helpful actions from the industry are insufficient as long as they simultaneously promote pesticides as though they were harmless panaceas. The most important question is how the attitudes and practices of IPM can be implemented in the Third World, especially among small and marginal farmers, and the constraints to such implementation removed.

Before going on to discuss the constraints operating against the widespread introduction of IPM, and how the techniques might be applied in the interests of poor farmers, it is useful to look briefly at how far IPM has been implemented in the Third World and at some examples of IPM in practice.

IPM in Practice

The extent to which implementation of integrated pest management programmes has progressed in the Third World is very disappointing. Indian journalist Bharat Dogra reports that:

"Integrated pest control is theoretically talked about by officials, and some of its constituents, such as growing disease resistant crops, are certainly attempted, but this has not become a reality on a large scale."[11]

This appears to be the general picture. Farmers rarely receive any advice on the use of non-chemical methods of pest management and where IPM programmes do exist they are usually applied to the production of plantation and cash crops, and to large landholdings, often as a response to a pesticide crisis. The 1977 OECD report says that

"despite the many benefits of this approach, IPM is not yet in widespread use".[12]

Despite the problems, though, some progress has been made either through local initiatives, through the activities of the FAO/UNEP Co-operative Global Programme for the Development and Application of Integrated Pest Control in Agriculture, or through other programmes, most notably the University of California/USAID Pest Management and Related Environmental Protection Project, now called the Consortium for International Crop Protection. The UK aid programme, through the Centre for Overseas Pest Research, offers training courses in the Third World in Pesticide Management. In general, though, progress has been remarkably slow. FAO's first symposium on IPM was held in 1965, and its panel of experts established in 1966. This group was involved in devising an IPM programme for cotton in Nicaragua. It was not until 1974, however, that the FAO/UNEP Global Programme was proposed, the activities of which remain at a relatively early stage of implementation.

While recognising how appallingly limited the dissemination of IPM remains, it is useful to look briefly at some projects which do exist in order to see how real is the potential, and also to highlight some of the pitfalls.

Malaysia — oil palm and cocoa

In Malaysia, by the early 1960s, the application of DDT, aldrin and dieldrin had led to serious pest outbreaks on oil palm and cocoa.[13] On oil palm, occasional spraying against bagworms and nettle caterpillars led to a treadmill so that these occasional pests became constant ones. "The more insecticide was used," says DeBach, "the worse the problem became."[14] Eventually, crop losses of 40% occurred despite spraying. Field studies led to the reinstatement of control by natural enemies, supplemented where necessary by applications of the more selective insecticide, trichlorphon. Spectacular improvements resulted here and in cocoa where events had been similar. In the latter case the use of dieldrin had led to outbreaks of caterpillars and finally to a treadmill involving the appearance of several more pests. When spraying was stopped, the natural enemies began to re-assert themselves and remaining pests were dealt with by selective application of trichlorphon. Meanwhile, it was discovered that the original pest — the bark borer — inhabited a native tree species. Removal of this tree from the cocoa plantations solved the bark borer problem.

Central America — cotton

Earlier chapters have described the ill-effects of pesticide use on cotton in Central America. A major source of information is the comprehensive study carried out by the Central American Research Institute for Industry — the ICAITI Report. The report states that:

"Since its inception this project has advocated the use of alternative cotton pest management procedures as a major solution to pesticide problems. Specifically, the project has emphasised the development of integrated cotton pest control as a technically feasible and economically profitable way to promote a more rational use of pesticides."[15]

With the aim of demonstrating this point, of training some people in IPM, and of generating interest in the IPM concept in Central America, ICAITI set up demonstrations which in their second year covered 0.3% of the cotton area of the region — 1,357 hectares. These plots were compared with neighbouring plots using conventional methods. The IPM programme incorporated monitoring, manual collection of pests, trap crops, control of weeds, careful choice of planting dates according to the phase of the moon (bollworm activity was found to be inhibited by a full moon), control of plant density and fertilizer application, and biological control by the release of *Trichogramma* wasps. Pesticide applications were made when necessary, taking account of the fact that a certain amount of 'fruit' could be lost with no effect on final yields. Economic damage thresholds were also determined and applied.

This amounted to quite a complex programme requiring considerable supervision. Nevertheless, its results effectively demonstrated the potential of IPM in the Third World context. Not only did the IPM plots produce higher yields with fewer pesticide applications; they also managed to reduce the number of applications in the second year, while on the conventional plots there was a dramatic *increase* in applications. The results speak for themselves:

Table 6
Central America: Yields and Pesticide Applications in Integrated Control Plots and Check Plots in Two Successive Years 1974/5 and 1975/6

	1974/5		1975/6	
	Kg/ha Seedcotton Yield	Pesticide Applications	Kg/ha Seedcotton Yield	Pesticide Applications
Integrated Control	3,310.5	15.7	3,408	14.8
Conventional Comparison	2,993	22.5	3,048	27.5
Source: ICAITI, Table 48, p. 147				

In one year, pesticide applications were reduced by 32%, with no loss of yield. Pest control costs per hectare, and per kilogram of cotton produced, were significantly lower and profits were three times higher than on conventional plots. In the second year the results were even more marked. The two-year average showed yields 11% higher with 39% fewer pesticide applications.

"This shows the effects of experience and confidence on the part of the growers who experienced the demonstration in their own lands."[16]

When the demonstration ended, some of the large farmers who had been involved hired IPM technicians and continued with the technique. ICAITI's conclusions were that,

"Integrated pest control results in significantly lower use of insecticides. There are potential environmental benefits to be derived from this reduction. The emphasis on low-toxicity products will have immediate benefits for the human health of the Central American population... In order to expand integrated control it will be necessary to devote considerable effort to increased demonstrations and dissemination of existing results. The present project has only begun to scratch the surface of the real problem, which is to change pest management practices in Central America."[17]

In Chapter 2 it was seen how the pesticide treadmill contributed to a crisis in the cotton fields of Nicaragua in the late 1960s and early 1970s. The problems were summarised in a report of the FAO Panel of Experts on Integrated Pest Control, meeting in 1974.

"During the 1965-66 growing season, cotton yields per ha. began to decline, reaching a 10 year low in the 1969-70 season. Simultaneously, production costs increased and cotton farming brought monetary losses to many farmers. The area planted to cotton declined to 40% of its previous peak between the 1967-68 and 1970-71 seasons. Cotton exports dropped significantly... This situation resulted in an unfavourable balance of trade for Nicaragua beginning in 1966. Furthermore, the land removed from cotton production became idle, resulting in loss of income for farm workers and high unemployment."[18]

With technical advice from FAO and funds from the UN Development Programme (UNDP) an IPM strategy was initiated in 1970 with the objective of reducing excessive pesticide use and minimising undesirable side-effects as well as of producing more cotton at a lower cost.

Supervised procedures based on monitoring replaced calendar spraying. Spray regimes were aimed at protecting beneficial species and these natural controls were augmented by the release of *Trichogramma*. The average number of insecticide applications per season fell from 28 in 1967-68 to 22 in 1970-71 and 18 in 1971-72.[19] By 1975 pesticides applied per hectare were reduced to 49 kgs compared to 80 in Guatemala and 70 in El Salvador.[20] In 1969-70 there were 383 deaths and over 3,000 cases of pesticide poisoning.[21] The number of cases fell to 557 in 1972 and 136 in 1974.[22]

The programme was not, however, an unqualified success. The 1974 FAO report stated that:

"Despite a leaning to integrated control, cotton farmers still rely heavily on the intensive use of synthetic organic insecticides for pest control. The high level of use contributes significantly to (1) production costs (20% to 50% of the total) and (2) environmental pollution."[23]

132

The report made a number of recommendations including a tax on the sale of pesticides and restrictions on the activities of pesticide salesmen. They further recommend strict government controls on chemicals presenting a hazard to humans, beneficial organisms and the environment.[24]

In 1977, the ICAITI report pointed to a number of other difficulties, particularly a failure to reach the smaller farmers. The major problems involved lack of financial support and, associated with this, a kind of brain-drain, where technicians trained for the IPM programme were hired away by international institutions for large private growers. The 80% of farmers who worked less than 35 hectares each were unable to get the technical assistance they needed. In short, the programme failed to take account of the agrarian structures of the country and so did not take the measures necessary to reach the smaller farmers.[25] The ICAITI report made recommendations for reaching small farmers, whereby existing technicians would be assigned small areas of 400-850 hectares and work with the farmers in the implementation of IPM. Eventually the programme would become self-supporting as the farmers became aware of the benefits.

The discussion of the Nicaragua experience raises a crucial issue in the implementation of IPM: it must be deliberately geared to reach the small farmer, who could otherwise be left behind and still further disadvantaged. Because IPM works most effectively when compatible methods cover a large area, its implementation among small farmers presents the additional serious difficulty of encouraging a large number of independent individuals to work together in a co-ordinated fashion for their mutual benefit.

China — cotton and rice

In China the practice of integrated pest control techniques stems from as long ago as the Third Century.[26] Today IPM is widely used in China, especially in cotton and rice production. In the Nanjing area about 10% of cotton-growing communes use IPM. Methods used for both cotton and rice include seed selection and timing of planting. On the shores of a lake at Suzhou, for example, there was once only one rice crop a year, which suffered severe pest problems in the later stages of growth. New seed strains were introduced which ripen earlier, thus both avoiding the pests and allowing time for a second rice crop. Other methods used include trap crops and the use of light traps to catch insects for monitoring purposes. Spraying is then determined on the basis of pre-determined threshold levels. Most communes use some combination of these methods and one member of each Production Team (50-60 adult workers) is responsible for monitoring. In turn, each Production Brigade (2-3 Teams) has its own research group. In Chiangsu Province loss of rice due to pests is claimed to be down to just 1%.[27]

In Tahsia People's Commune, near Kwangchow,

> "The combination of cultural practices, light traps, use of
> *Trichogramma* and *Bacillus thuringiensis,* preservation of the
> existing natural enemy population, and the introduction of insect-
> eating ducks have led to a great reduction in the use of chemical
> pesticides. The cost of control has decreased by 85%."[28]

In 1972 the Chiaohsu People's Commune started an IPM programme for rice. Commune members were mobilized to kill insects in all stages of farm work. Biological methods, including the use of *Trichogramma,* were also employed, as

Rothampsted light trap.

were light traps. Over 2,000 people were involved in a pest control network. The commune set up its own workshop to propagate *Trichogramma*. Insecticide use fell 64% from 159 tons in 1972 to 58 tons in 1976, with improvements continuing.[29]

Boel Berner, who visited China with a Swedish group investigating pest control, concluded that, while the technical components were important,

"The dedication and knowledge of the peasants and technicians involved, and the efficiency of the organisation for pest forecasting and for the distribution of new methods and ideas to the peasants, are even more important."

Berner attributed the Chinese success in implementing IPM to "strong political support for the integrated control approach".[30]

IPM fits in with the Chinese emphasis on self-reliance. In addition, since IPM methods are more labour intensive, "people who might otherwise have been unemployed or under-employed, can find useful labour".[31]

IPM works most effectively on an area basis, with many farmers following compatible practices such as sowing their crops synchronously. The Chinese agrarian system is conductive to this aspect of IPM.

It seems that Chinese agriculture has particular advantages for the incorporation of IPM which are not always present in other Third World countries. The Chinese experience emphasises the need for efficient organisation, community participation and strong political will as vital factors in the implementation of IPM in the Third World. Nevertheless, the Chinese experience indicates, too, that IPM is not a technique suitable only for rich countries and, indeed, that it is in many ways particularly appropriate for poor countries because it is labour intensive and accords with aspirations towards self-reliance. Although Chinese conditions are perhaps unique, small farmers in a number of Third World countries have traditions of community co-operation and organisations which foster such traditions. These could act as an effective background for the development of the IPM approach.

India — rice and cotton

In India, experimental IPM programmes for rice have been carried out since 1975 at six locations in five States. At each location nearby villages using IPM and conventional pest control are compared. The largest project is in Cuttack district in Orissa where eleven villages with an area of 2,500 acres under IPM are compared with a 300 acre control village.[32] The project stresses the importance of gearing control measures to individual plots, where rice is grown by a large number of small farmers. Pest populations are monitored by the project team and by the use of light traps by individual farmers. On the basis of such monitoring, insecticides are applied according to pre-determined threshold levels. Cultural methods used include ploughing in of stubble, adjustment of planting times and avoidance of over-fertilization. Pesticides are chosen and applied so as to inflict minimum damage on natural enemies. Varieties resistant to some of the major pests are also used.

The project is explicitly inter-disciplinary and attempts to take full account of "the socio-economic constraints operating in adoption of the modern technology by rice farmers".[33] The farmers are directly involved in the project through monitoring and through weekly training classes.

"The main emphasis of the programme is to train the farmers themselves to use the pest management programme so that they become self-reliant in the use of the technology rather than depending on experts."[34]

The results have been encouraging. During the rabi (October to January) season of 1979 the major pest, stem borer, reached the economic injury level in only one of the eleven villages.

The project's 1979 Annual Report stated that,

"The major gain of integrated pest management programmes in the area has been a drastic cut in the number of insecticide applications from an average of 4-6 rounds of sprays given prior to commencement of the project to an average of two rounds per crop."[35]

There have also been some schemes for IPM in cotton in India. In one case pesticide applications were reduced from an average of 17 down to 9, while yields increased. One of the organisers of this programme was Dr. Bill Reed, an entomologist at the International Crops Research Institute for the Semi-Arid Tropics (ICRISAT). He analyses the success of the scheme:

"All farmers in the village agreed to co-operate. Perhaps the most important step was synchronous sowing at the optimum time. Sprays were applied according to pest counts and all farmers uprooted their crop at the end of the season."[36]

Constraints against IPM

IPM appears to present such a clearly preferable approach that it may seem strange that it is not already universally adopted. The most common explanation is that IPM requires a level of knowledge, expertise and infrastructure which is presently unavailable in most Third World countries. In order to implement an IPM programme, goes this argument, the farmer requires specialist assistance, analogous to a doctor who can diagnose a complaint and prescribe treatment. The lack of such specialists has led many in the Third World to see IPM merely as a hope for tomorrow.

This attitude, although understandable, is unfortunate in that it may condemn countries in which it prevails to the problems of unmitigated reliance on pesticides -- a technology whose proper, safe and effective use also requires a considerable degree of expertise, infrastructure and equipment. Nevertheless, it is true that a complete IPM programme does require research, expertise and infrastructure as well as some degree of community organisation. Where research and extension services are inadequate and under-financed, this can be a serious constraint on the effective implementation of IPM among small farmers. These are, though, not insuperable obstacles. In a number of Third World countries the expertise already exists and the application of sufficient funds and political will could mobilize it.

It is ironic then, that IPM programmes, and particularly the element involving training, should be constrained by lack of funds. In February 1981 Dr. Lucas Brader, Chief of the Plant Protection Service of FAO, had this to say:

"FAO is giving very strong support to the development of integrated pest management as the best means for safer pesticide use. We have quite a number of ongoing projects in the field but the major problem is finding the necessary financial support... In fact we have a substantial number of draft projects ready on paper but cannot implement them due to lack of funds."[37]

One example is the Near East Inter-Country Programme for IPM in cotton. In December 1979 the FAO/UNEP Panel of Experts on IPM noted that, "The Training/Liaison Officer post could not be established for lack of funds".[38]

This is in spite of the Expert Committee's recommendations that training, especially at field level, should be given the highest priority.[39]

This brings us to the third major constraint on the implementation of IPM in the Third World. In addition to lack of expertise and funds, there appears to be a lack of political will on the part of governments of both the West and the Third World. It takes courage to launch a long-term programme aimed at reducing the ill-effects of pesticide dependence through IPM when pesticides promise, and may deliver in the short term, the kind of quick and easy results so attractive to politicians and many of their electorates. For a rich country government, it must seem only too easy to let the industry worry about pest control problems in the Third World, rather than aiding the promotion of IPM and exercising control over pesticide exports. Similarly, a Third World government faced with shortages of money and resources may find it easier to leave it to the pesticide salesmen than to mount effective agricultural extension programmes to advise farmers of the alternatives. The difficult path of attempting to enforce legislation restricting the activities of powerful international companies is also one which Third World governments may, understandably, prefer to avoid.

It would be preferable if international public and expert opinion could outweigh such political inertia before governments are driven to act by pest control crises, which until now have been the greatest force working in favour of IPM.

Pesticides themselves, the promise they offer of an easy life, their tendency to produce addiction through the action of the treadmill, and their promotion by wealthy and powerful interests, form one of the main constraints operating against IPM.

Describing insecticides as "habit-forming" and "narcotic-like", entomologist DeBach has this to say:

> "Even after the answers are known regarding the degree of unnecessary use of pesticides and their adverse effects, and after research has shown to what extent effective natural enemies of the various pests are present, it is not necessarily an automatic or easy matter to switch to integrated control from a heavy chemical program."[40]

This difficulty strengthens the imperative that IPM should begin to be implemented before rather than after chemical dependence leads to disaster. This also gives the Third World, and especially small farmers, an advantage in the implementation of IPM since they are, so far, at a relatively early stage of addiction. This advantage, though, must be seized before it is lost.

Implementing IPM for the Poor

IPM itself is not a panacea. The implementation of IPM in the Third World must proceed urgently, but unless it is carried out sensitively and with the fullest possible participation of farmers, it will not succeed and it will not help the poor. IPM must not be seen in terms of a sudden switch to an imported and complete system of pest control. Professor Ray F. Smith has defined IPM in terms of what it is *not*:

> "It is not the development over a long period of time, with much research effort, of a completely new pest control system which then is established in place of the old system; rather the process is a series of incremental steps which gradually modify the old existing system."[41]

Whether the existing system is a traditional one, or a pesticide-dependent one, the implementation of IPM can only proceed cautiously and with the complete involvement of local communities. In the former case, the IPM approach needs to be introduced before the community steps onto the pesticide road. If this approach is based on a traditional system which is working reasonably effectively, little immediate change may be necessary, but the approach can help to prevent the adoption of a pesticide-dependent strategy. In this case implementation of IPM may eventually involve the actual introduction of pesticides ·· but this would, by that time, be firmly within the IPM context. For the most part, though, IPM will be most urgently needed in situations where pest attack is relatively severe and where traditional methods alone have been unable to cope. In such situations, it is likely that pesticides will already be in use, often in an indiscriminate, uncontrolled and hazardous fashion. Indeed, in the most urgent cases, pesticide use will be a major contributor to the farmers' problems. To date most IPM projects in the Third World have been implemented in situations of pesticide-induced crisis. Such crises provide the powerful motivation needed to overcome the constraints operating against IPM.

Implementation of IPM in the Third World must be based on a close co-ordination between research, training and technical assistance, carried out as far as possible by local people right from the start. The information and methods must be disseminated in the community in understandable language and this must be a two-way process. Farmers' knowledge of their land and methods of agriculture and pest control should form the basis on which the IPM programme is devised.

The research necessary for a fully developed IPM programme requires facilities and expertise often unavailable in the Third World, especially to the poor farmer. This dilemma has led Third World decision-makers to turn their backs on IPM and go for the apparently easier pesticide solution. Professor Ray Smith explains the step-wise approach which overcomes this dilemma:

> "To this we can say that to our knowledge, every operational integrated pest control system in existence today has in fact had a relatively simple yet effective beginning.
>
> The first programs were a best approximation of an ideal system based on the then available knowledge... In this way, even where resources are rather limited, an effective integrated control system can often be developed and adapted to the local situation... Integrated pest control holds much promise for becoming the conceptual basis for all pest control of the future."[42]

The 1977 OECD report on pest control for small food crop farmers in the Third World describes how this step-wise approach may operate in the small farmer context. The example given shows the first step to be the fullest use of cultural controls, especially crop sanitation and planting dates. Step 2 involves the careful choice of type and dosage of pesticides, in order to minimise damage to natural enemies and to protect farmworkers.

The third step introduces monitoring and allows pesticide applications to be timed according to economic damage thresholds.

Next comes an analysis of the natural enemies with a view to their integration into the control system. Next, a forecasting system could be developed over a fairly wide area as a basis for prompt action when necessary.

The final steps involve the introduction of other control measures such as biological control through mass-produced enemies and the breeding and use of pest resistant plant varieties.

The research, extension, training and communication processes are developed simultaneously. This approach is not a blueprint but rather an example of the way such a scheme could progress.

It may be argued that, at least up to step 3, this is not IPM but rather some kind of 'supervised control'. Such an argument, though essentially true, is a little pedantic since, as Professor Way of Imperial College, London, says, such practices "are the critically important first step in the development of most integrated control procedures".[43]

Such 'supervised control' is the first move, at the farmer level, in dealing with the problems of pesticide misuse. Such misuse cannot wait for a fully developed IPM programme before it is dealt with. At the same time complementary action must be taken at the regulatory level to safeguard farmers and encourage IPM.

The Role of Traditional Pest Control Methods

In training, research and implementation of IPM, the importance of beginning with traditional practices has already been stressed. In a newspaper interview in the US, Smith was asked why, if IPM is so simple and logical, it had not been tried before. His reply was:

"It has — it's old traditional agriculture with a little bit of sophistication added."[44]

The arrival of pesticides on the scene has though, led to the demise of many of these traditional methods. The Farmers Assistance Board (FAB) of the Philippines have said:

"With the encroachment of the pesticide business and with the help of government legislation, the traditional methods of pest control are suppressed and to a greater extent almost wiped out of existence."[45]

FAB go on to list 29 different traditional methods gathered from just one village. No doubt some of these are effective and others are not, but there is apparently an extensive basis here on which to begin a pest management system which would not make farmers' local knowledge redundant.

Dr. Bill Reed of ICRISAT described the value of some traditional methods and the way in which they have fallen into disuse with the arrival of pesticides:

"In the semi-dry tropics the dry/hot seasons kill most pests by depriving them of food. In the wet tropics, rain itself reduces pest numbers. Most farmers unconsciously took advantage of such reductions by sowing on traditional dates. Evolution and selection ensured that the plants they grew and the timing of sowing and maturity were optimal to maximise yields and minimise losses to pests and other yield reducers. These were the bases of IPM, traditional style. In addition sowing dates across areas were synchronised so pests were diluted across the area rather than concentrated on small areas of early sown where they had a chance to multiply then disperse to late sown crops. Natural selection ensured that farmers (and crops) that did not stick to the seasons were eliminated.

Pesticides have destroyed 'traditional IPM' in some areas, particularly on cotton. Pesticides allow sequential sowing without obvious penalty."[46]

FAO's model extension leaflet on pest resistance to pesticides encourages the re-emphasis of methods such as crop rotation, host-free periods (fallow periods between crops), destruction of wild plants which are the sources of pest infestation, selection of planting times and the destruction of stubble.[47] Other methods include mixed cropping systems where two or more crops are grown simultaneously or alternately. Such systems have evolved over the years by trial and error and can be very effective. In Northern Nigeria, for example, cowpeas alone produce virtually no crop without pesticides, but in a mixed cropping system produce useful yields even with no pesticide treatment at all.[48]

It is also worth mentioning that traditional agriculture often included the use of some locally available 'pesticides' such as soap or tobacco. These have the advantage of being cheap and easily available, but are not necessarily safer for the farmer to use. Nicotine (from tobacco), for example, is classified by WHO in class 1B, 'highly hazardous'. Its LD_{50} is 50 mg/kg both orally and through the unbroken skin.

The role of traditional practices in IPM has been summed up by the OECD report on pest control for small farmers.

"It is now becoming apparent that many of the traditional approaches and techniques used by small farmers should be preserved as far as possible because they are the results of a long evolutionary process and experience and it is clear that many of these traditional practices can be employed as elements in a well-balanced crop protection system... The pest management approach is likely to appeal to small farmers particularly because in many cases it is able to incorporate their traditional techniques and these should always be investigated as providing a potential sound basis for crop protection..."[49]

IPM for Today

The examples we have looked at of the implementation of IPM in the Third World demonstrate its usefulness, not tomorrow, but today. To begin implementing IPM, although it requires skilled personnel for research, planning and supervision, "does not demand a *total* knowledge in advance of all components in the system — only an adequate one,"[50]   says Dr. Haskell, Director of Britain's Centre for Overseas Pest Research. The idea that such total knowledge and

140

expertise are prerequisites for IPM would make its implementation very slow and would restrict it largely to high value plantation crops. For the rest it would be seen only as a long-term aim. According to Haskell,

> "this is indeed one opinion of the position and one which accounts for the view that integrated pest control is for tomorrow not today... if the phrase 'long-term aim' is taken to mean, as it often is, that implementation of integrated control must be delayed for years while studies of the basic ecology of the pest/crop complex are undertaken, this view must be challenged on the grounds of experience that even partial utilization of the concept can bring important advantages in reduction of cost and of ecological and environmental damage. Particularly in relation to tropical problems, it overlooks the rapid rate at which deterioriation in control due to continued reliance on a single component system using broad spectrum insecticides can occur, the 'disaster phase'... often appearing only a year or two after a period when, literally, 'everything in the garden looked lovely'. The *well documented disasters... surely emphasize that we must be prepared, particularly in tropical agriculture, to implement tomorrow's methods today or risk an increasing number of disasters in the precise area where they can be afforded least."* (our emphasis)[51]

Haskell concludes that while

> "it would be foolish to pretend that integrated control is a panacea for all plant protection problems... The arguments.. show that integrated control can be applied *now* with advantage to small farmer food crops and that the time is ripe to do this, at the same time disposing of the view that this is too complicated and too long-term a technique to implement immediately. On the contrary.. *its wider use is already overdue."* (our emphasis)[52]

Haskell expressed this powerful view in 1977. Yet, while there have been some isolated achievements, the disasters continue while IPM remains, for almost all Third World farmers, a dream for the future, of which they have never heard. Urgent action must be taken now, and this is perhaps the greatest contribution which people and governments in rich countries can make to IPM, to remove the constraints which allow the pesticide strategy to expand virtually unchallenged in the Third World. At the same time the fullest support must be given to all initiatives to implement the IPM philosophy in partnership with the poor and in a complementary relationship with other health, agricultural and social development initiatives.

The pesticide industry in particular has the potential to make a positive contribution through the development of selective pesticides appropriate to IPM and of improved application equipment. Some companies are already working in these fields. The industry could also contribute through the dissemination of attitudes consistent with the IPM approach. Companies, though, need to sell their products in order to remain in business and it is perhaps understandable that sales sometimes take priority over the promotion of the IPM philosophy. The British Agrochemicals Association have themselves stressed this point. Whilst they favour an international code of advertising practice, they point out that there is "no getting away from the fact that companies will promote what they have to sell through the medium of advertising. Good agricultural practice, integrated methods of pest management are unlikely to feature in advertisements unless they help to promote the product in question."[53]

For these reasons, although industry can do much on a voluntary basis, it is also necessary for governments and international organisations to build up an appropriate regulatory framework which will be conducive to IPM and to the safe and judicious use of pesticides. This framework should include controls on marketing and pesticide exports in order to ensure the international transfer of information and to help Third World governments to regulate pesticides more effectively. These matters are dealt with more fully in the next chapter.

The Present Controls and Future Needs

THE PRESENT CONTROLS AND FUTURE NEEDS

Individual pesticide users have responsiblity for their own safety and should ensure as far as possible that they use the products in accordance with sensible and recommended standards. They are able to exercise these responsibilities, however, only insofar as they have access to full, correct and usable information. In the Third World such information is often not available, especially to small farmers and farm labourers. Lack of literacy, equipment and services and a harsh environment make it difficult for users to follow even the advice they are given.

Under these circumstances a primary responsibility for the safety and health of Third World farmers and farmworkers must lie with their employers and with their own governments. The primary responsibility for protecting the Third World consumer and environment and for defining national policies with regard to agriculture must similarly lie with the appropriate authorities in each Third World country.

Even if these duties were fully accepted and acted upon, though, there would remain a heavy burden of responsibility on the exporting countries and on the companies producing and marketing pesticides. These latter responsibilities are increased and made more critical to the extent that Third World governments and employers fail, or are unable, to fulfil their own obligations effectively.

Ideally Third World governments should enact strict legislative controls over the import, formulation, distribution, advertising, promotion and use of pesticides. In addition, they should ensure adequate resources for effective enforcement of this legislation. Legislation should be complemented by an efficient and well-trained agricultural research, training and extension service especially geared to the needs of small and marginal farmers and farm labourers. In order for all these measures to be fully effective, other social and political measures would be necessary to improve the status of the rural poor through, for example, greater investment in the countryside and the redistribution of land. Finally, there should be a primary health care system closely allied with the agricultural extension service and including specifically occupational health care — especially the prevention, recognition and treatment of pesticide poisoning.

Such comprehensive policies for the prevention and remedy of pesticide-related problems do not exist even in the richest countries and can hardly be expected to exist in the poorest, although help and encouragement are available through such initiatives as WHO's Global Medium-term Programme for Workers' Health, and FAO's Integrated Pest Control programmes.

Third World Controls

Despite the difficulties and lack of resources, a number of Third World countries have enacted some legislation for the control of pesticides. Such legislation varies from comprehensive to rudimentary, and enforcement is often slow, difficult and patchy. A recent attempt by FAO to categorise the degree of sophistication of pesticide control measures in member countries produced the following classification:

Table 7	
Countries with well developed procedures, usually involving wide technical requirements and legal maximum residue limits in food.	24 countries (including 22 OECD members, 9 EEC members)
Countries with well developed procedures, strictly state-controlled.	7 countries
Countries where control measures are known to exist, but information is not available on extent or efficiency.	26 countries
Countries believed to be in the process of introducing some control procedures.	6 countries
Countries from where there is no information or that are known not to have control procedures.	81 countries

Source: J.A.R. Bates, Pesticide Residues Specialist, Plant Protection Service, FAO, "Pesticides — Constraints and Controls in Importing Countries", paper for International Seminar on Controls of Chemicals in Importing Countries, Dubrovnik, 22-24 April 1981, p. 14.

FAO pesticides officer A.V. Adam wrote in 1976 that 40% of developing countries were estimated to have no specific legislation and added the important rider that: "even where they do, individual schemes are inadequate".[1]

Bearing these general trends in mind, it is worth looking at some specific examples of Third World countries' attempts to control pesticides by legislation.

Sri Lanka's new legislation (the Control of Pesticides Act) was certified on 5 September 1980.[2] It provides for the appointment of a Registrar and a Formulary Committee, responsible for the licensing of pesticide formulations. Manufacturers have to give comprehensive information in the licence application, which may be rejected, provisionally granted for limited use or granted. Licensing conditions specify that the label must be in all of Sri Lanka's three languages (Sinhala, Tamil and English) and must include the common name of the active ingredients, use directions, waiting periods, warnings and first aid information. The container must be safe and only the approved container and label can be used. Pesticides must be kept away from foodstuffs in transport and in shops. Leaflets with the pesticide must contain all the label particulars and it will be illegal to advertise "in a manner that is false, misleading or deceptive". Contravention of the act carries a penalty of two years' imprisonment.

In September 1980, a list of approved pesticides published in 1979 was in use, but the regulations specified under the Act had yet to be made and enforced. The approved list contains a number of extremely hazardous pesticides, some of which are banned or restricted in the West.[3] Regulations to restrict the uses of these had yet to be drawn up.

Sri Lanka is to be commended for enacting such comprehensive legislation, but it remains to be seen how far it will be enforced. In addition, the act will not be effective unless it is backed up by education of workers, availability of equipment, effective agricultural extension and health services, and the research capacity to monitor the requirements of the Act. The Government will also have to keep in touch with scientific and regulatory developments in other countries, especially in Europe and America, in order to amend its legislation in the light of new findings and experience. Finally, the regulations must take account of the reality of work in the fields, and so representatives of cultivators and labourers should be included in the regulatory process.

Malaysia's experience could well point to the difficulties which lie ahead for Sri Lanka. In Malaysia, the Pesticides Act was passed in 1974, but enforcement could not begin until April 1981.[4] The effects and stringency of its enforcement are still to be seen. If the Act is strictly enforced, though, it could bring great benefits. The Act covers many aspects of the control of pesticides including registration and labelling. The requirements for warnings on labels are particularly strict, requiring different coloured bands for different hazard groups, and a skull and crossbones symbol for the most hazardous. Five classes are defined by hazard, based on the WHO classification. The legislation also lays down special requirements for particular pesticides. For example, paraquat must contain a stinking agent and the dioxin content of 2,4,5-T is limited. In particular, the Act recognises the dangers of uncontrolled advertising and certain statements have been forbidden.[5] This is ambitious legislation, and Malaysia, as one of the better off Third World countries, may have the resources to enforce it.

In Zimbabwe, regulations exist to control the sale, labelling, packaging and advertising of pesticides, and further regulations are awaiting enforcement. These regulations state that certain pesticides, including 2,4,5-T and paraquat and those with an LD_{50} below 100mg/kg, may only be used where appropriate protective clothing is worn and first aid available. However, hazardous pesticides are still available, including many banned in Europe and the USA. Ministry officials admit that legislative control of the use of pesticides is difficult to implement.[6]

Problems of enforcement are indeed widespread in Third World countries. It was reported in July 1981, for example, that a survey had been carried out in India, ordered by the Agriculture Minister, to check on the enforcement of quality standards under the Central Insecticides Act. Ninety-eight samples were taken in the three States of Uttar Pardesh, Bihar and Madhya Pradesh, of which 57 were found to be substandard, including 45% of those marked as conforming to the standards of the Indian Standards Institute.[7]

In Kenya pesticides are affected by a number of pieces of legislation, although most were not drafted specifically with pesticides in mind. David Kinyanjui of the National Environment Secretariat concludes that "the protection offered by current legislation is, to say the least, vague and inadequate"[8] and that, indeed, "it is evident that legislation on pesticides *per se* does not exist on a national basis in the country".[9] Kinyanjui proposes new legislation and a properly regulated system to bring marketing and distribution of pesticides under government control.

> "The present practice whereby chemical firms advertise and directly sell their pesticide products to farmers should be discouraged and if possible eliminated."[10]

In Thailand the relevant legislation is contained in the Poisonous Article Acts (PAA) of 1967 and 1973. These are not specific to pesticides. The Acts classify poisonous articles into two categories: 'ordinary' and 'highly'poisonous articles, the only apparent difference being in the fees payable to obtain the permits required for import, export, manufacture or sale. The regulations include a registration requirement and some controls on labelling, advertising and aerial spraying.[11]

The problem of the Thai legislation were described by Banpot Napompeth, Director of the Biological Control Research Center in 1980:

> "No surveillance and inspection procedures have been established in a clear and rigid way yet... With improper interpretation and tactical exploitation of the present Acts... on the provisions relating to import and export control, Thailand could also serve as a potential dumping ground for pesticides banned elsewhere... When subject to critical review, both PAA 1967 and PAA 1973 are environmentally unsound and further immediate revision and amendment are required... Other than being ineffective in preventing the influx of pesticides... the Acts do not provide adequate regulations to prevent the contamination of farm products."[12]

The overall situation has been well summed-up by Faith Campbell of the Natural Resources Defense Council in the US. Giving evidence to the US Government Sub-committee on International Economic Policy and Trade, she had this to say:

> "Some developing countries have enacted virtually no legislation to govern the importation, domestic use and disposal of potentially toxic chemicals, and few maintain any facilities for monitoring the effects of the products on health or the environment. Even where decent laws are on the books, many governments lack the technical and administrative capacity to implement them."[13]

This lack of effective control in many Third World countries adds to the moral imperative which should govern the policies of pesticide exporting countries. Such policies should recognise that,

> "The use of chemicals has spread much more quickly throughout the developing world than has the capability to assure their safe use".[14]

It should also be recognised that export controls should be sufficiently flexible and consultative to avoid the straight imposition of one country's standards upon another. Different countries do have different priorities and needs and legislation must allow for these.

Third World Views

The moral imperative demanding Western action to control the export of banned, restricted and hazardous pesticides, is also backed up by a chorus of voices from the Third World and from international organisations. It has been argued that export controls are not wanted by Third World people.

"Lesser developed countries," says F.J. Rarig of the Rohm and Haas Company, "demand the right to destroy their existing culture and to join us in the perilous adventure of exploiting high technology.
... Those who urge the reduction of the impact of pesticides on the world environment do not speak for the lesser developed countries."[15]

On the contrary, many representatives of governmental and non-governmental organisations in the Third World have strongly expressed a desire that the exporting countries act to control pesticide exports and exchange information about pesticides banned or restricted in their countries of origin. It is worth remembering that the term 'banned' is often used to include "a hazardous chemical significantly restricted for use in a particular country".[16]

At the same conference as Rarig made his pronouncement, Mr Samuel Gitonga, Chief Agriculturalist for the National Irrigation Board of Kenya, had this to say:

"We do not have the necessary machinery to go through an entire testing program to determine whether the product is safe or not. For these reasons, I believe that the US and other developed countries have a responsibility to ensure that the information they have painfully gathered is made available to as many people as possible in the developing world. I certainly reject the idea that the developing countries always know what they want or which pesticides are best to use. Information that a product is not allowed for use in a particular country would be a very useful starting point. The less developed countries must be made aware that there is a problem with using a particular product ... *These very real dangers of incompletely tested or banned products being used in the less developed countries should be strongly condemned by the international community, and efforts should be made to see how they can be avoided* ... I would like to stress my point that *the developed countries have a clear responsibility* to provide the less developed with information on pesticide registrations, suspensions, cancellations, and so forth ... There is also a need for more international co-operation in the control of international sales of pesticides. We must ensure that unsafe products are not sold, or at least that the governments importing these products know exactly what they are receiving."[17] (our emphasis)

Also, at the same meeting, Dr. Frank Del Prado, of the Ministry of Agriculture of Surinam, said:

"Of course we try to be as careful as possible but we still must depend on information received from importers who would like to sell their products ... No data on waiting periods are available to us ... We lack not only laboratory equipment but also trained personnel ... Something has to be done, and fast ... many products that can be sold to us do not comply with standards of quality, efficacy and safety ... Perhaps, through co-operation with the proper authorities in developed countries, something can be done for my country."[18]

Dr. J. C. Kiano, the Kenyan Minister for Water Development, urged in 1977 at a meeting of UNEP that

"unless a product has been adequately tested certified, and widely used in the countries of origin, it should not be used for export".[19]

A representative of the US General Accounting Office testified in 1978 that 14 countries had specifically told the agency that they wished to receive notification of US pesticide regulatory decisions.[20]

In July 1980, His Excellency A. A. Abbas, the Nigerian Ambassador to the US, wrote to the House Foreign Affairs Committee to pass on the statement of the Nigerian Ministry of Housing and Environment that

"This Ministry supports the move being discussed by the US Government to ban the exports of products (from US which have been found to be hazardous to the public health and are prohibited from use in the US), particularly with reference to Nigeria".[21]

In December 1978 the Central American Non-Governmental Conservation Societies Conference, held in Guatemala, adopted a resolution calling on its member organisations to send telegrams to President Carter with the following message:

"Seriously alarmed by the abuse and increasing use in our countries of chemical substances (pesticides, medications, food additives etc) which are prohibited by legislation in the United States, as well as other industrialised countries, we request in the name of human principle, that authorization be denied to the exportation of such products to our countries for use at the cost of our health and the lives of dozens of thousands of our fellow men. We request you to extend this protection to the rest of the humans of our planet and that you use your influence with other industrialised countries so that they will also follow suit to ensure the effectiveness of our request."[22]

In November 1980 31 consumer leaders from 13 countries signed the "Penang Declaration on the Export of Hazardous Substances and Facilities".[23] This declaration urged "all governments to establish export control programmes for hazardous substances". They specified that no distinction should be made between domestic and foreign consumers other than in specified exceptional circumstances. Such exceptions had to be demonstrated by the exporters and exporting country governments with full public participation.

UN Views

In August 1979 a workshop was held in Thailand for National Correspondents in the Asia and Pacific Regions of UNEP's International Register of Potentially Toxic Chemicals (IRPTC). The IRPTC National Correspondents are responsible for providing information for the register from their countries, for distributing information and for assisting IRPTC in answering queries from governments,

148

scientists and organisations around the world. They are usually senior government employees or academics. The IRPTC Bulletin reported on the Thai meeting, in which 16 countries participated:

"Strong views were expressed during the Workshop on the dangers of exporting chemicals banned in the country of manufacture to countries which did not have such bans and were not aware of such bans. These views were embodied in a recommendation which requested that the matter be brought again to the notice of the Governing Council of UNEP for appropriate action."[24]

In November 1980, IRPTC Correspondents in the Africa and West Asia Regions held a workshop in Nairobi. Twenty countries participated and again: "strong views were expressed ... on the problems of exporting to developing countries chemicals banned or restricted in their country of origin."[25]

In response to these and other views, the UNEP Governing Council has repeatedly added its voice to the clamour for export controls and information exchange on restricted chemicals. In 1977 the 58 nation Council urged

"governments to take steps to ensure that potentially harmful chemicals, in whatever form or commodity, which are unacceptable for domestic purposes in the exporting country, are not permitted to be exported without the prior knowledge and consent of appropriate authorities in the importing country".[26]

At the 1978 UNEP meeting the issue was raised again with expressions of concern coming from representatives of Kenya, Bangladesh, Ghana, Iran, Jamaica, Nigeria, Pakistan and the Philippines.[27] Another resolution was adopted appealing to exporting countries

"to prevent the export of items which are restricted, or not registered for use in the countries of origin until the exporting countries have ascertained that the results of tests and evaluations on the effects of these chemicals on the health of the people and the environment (as well as detailed instructions in mutually agreed languages for the safe use of these products) have been provided to the designated authorities in the recipient countries, so as to make it possible for these authorities to make fully informed decisions on the import and utilization of the products".[28]

The 1979 meeting

"again commented on the need to avoid the export of industrial processes and products which have harmful effects on health and the environment ... there should be information exchange between exporting and importing countries on trade in and properties of potentially toxic chemicals".[29]

Later in 1979 the UN General Assembly, at its 34th session, adopted a resolution urging

"member states to exchange information on hazardous chemicals ... that have been banned in their territories and to discourage, in consultation with importing countries, the exportation of such products to other countries".[30]

UNITED NATIONS

GENERAL
ASSEMBLY

Distr.
GENERAL

A/RES/34/173
18 January 1980

Thirty-fourth session
Agenda item 12

RESOLUTION ADOPTED BY THE GENERAL ASSEMBLY

/on the report of the Third Committee (A/34/829)/7

34/173. Exchange of information on banned hazardous
chemicals and unsafe pharmaceutical products

The General Assembly,

Aware that the exportation of banned hazardous chemicals and unsafe
pharmaceutical products could have serious and adverse effects on the health of
peoples in the importing countries,

Recognizing the urgent need to take concrete measures to prevent the adverse
effects on health on a world-wide basis and, to that end, mindful of the
importance of objective information about banned hazardous chemicals and unsafe
pharmaceutical products,

1. Urges Member States to exchange information on hazardous chemicals and
unsafe pharmaceutical products that have been banned in their territories and to
discourage, in consultation with importing countries, the exportation of such
products to other countries;

2. Requests the Secretary-General, in co-operation with the United Nations
agencies and bodies concerned, especially the World Health Organization, to assist
Governments in exchanging information and to submit a report to the General
Assembly at its thirty-fifth session, through the Economic and Social Council,
about the experience of Member States and the United Nations agencies and bodies
concerned.

106th plenary meeting
17 December 1979

80-01628

US Policy

In recent years the US Government has gone some way towards accepting a responsibility for the export of hazardous pesticides, and answering the numerous requests for action from Third World and international organisations. It has been discussed in Chapter 7, for example, how USAID has adopted procedures to safeguard Third World people from hazardous pesticides and to encourage the use of integrated pest management.

Under the Federal Insecticide, Fungicide and Rodenticide Act (FIFRA), as amended in 1978, the US has adopted certain rules governing pesticide exports. The detailed procedures under these rules were issued in July 1980.[31] Firstly, all pesticides for export have to be properly labelled in English and the language of the importing country. The other provisions cover only those pesticides which are not registered in the US or which are being exported for a use which is cancelled or suspended in the US. For these pesticides the foreign purchaser, prior to export, has to sign a statement acknowledging an understanding of the US regulatory status of the product. A copy of this signed statement is sent by the exporter to the US Environmental Protection Agency (EPA) which informs appropriate government officials in the importing country. Once aware of the import, these officials can ask EPA for additional information including available substitutes and so make an informed decision about their own actions. Only the first shipment to a particular country in a given year need be notified for each pesticide.[32]

By April 1981 EPA had sent 378 of these notifications to 134 countries and some Third World countries had taken the opportunity to ask for further information.[33] The FIFRA rules, though, do not include provisions to prevent the export taking place after consultation with the importing country. They are simply a means of ensuring some exchange of information.

Two initiatives have recently attempted to strengthen the US policy on the export of hazardous substances. In both cases the attempt was to bring together and strengthen the provisions of diverse statutes into a single coherent policy. In both cases this was intended to cover a wide range of hazardous substances — pharmaceuticals, consumer goods and others, as well as pesticides.

The Barnes Bill was a proposal for new legislation. Under the Bill products restricted by certain specific statutes would be forbidden from export unless granted a licence. Licensing conditions would provide for consultation with the importing country government, exchange of information and consideration of costs and benefits.[34]

The Barnes Bill was withdrawn in late 1980 in favour of the other initiative — an Executive Order by President Carter. This Order was signed by President Carter on 15 January 1981 and was official US policy for a month before it was revoked by President Reagan on 17 February. This policy was not new legislation, but rather a presidential interpretation of existing legislation, particularly of the Export Administration Act, 1979, which authorizes the President to restrict exports "where necessary to further significantly the foreign policy of the US or to fulfil its declared international obligations".[35]

Announcing the policy, President Carter said,

"As international merchants, we have an obligation not to export to unsuspecting nations products which we ourselves would not allow in our country".[36]

The Executive Order had four main parts:

- it regularised the notification procedures by providing that all notifications go through a single department and contain a minimum of information including relevant US regulations and details of the hazards which led to regulation;

- it provided for the annual publication of a summary of US regulations on hazardous substances, including actions pending;

- it directed US agencies, including the State Department, to participate actively in and encourage international efforts to improve information exchange on hazardous exports, and

- it established procedures for using the Export Administration Act to control exports of a small number of especially hazardous substances.

The Carter policy considered only 70 or so pesticide active ingredients for control, of which only a few would actually require licensing.[37] In these cases, licences would be granted only after consultation with the importing country government.[38] Following the revocation of this Executive Order by President Reagan, the Barnes Bill has been re-introduced into Congress. At the time of writing, though, the FIFRA procedures are the only specific measures governing US pesticide exports.

In view of the serious problems associated with pesticide use in the Third World and of the lack of effective legislative controls by Third World governments, it is very likely that mishaps in both health and agriculture will continue to occur in the Third World. This likelihood would be reduced if strict and effective controls were placed on pesticide exports by exporting country governments. The current prevailing norm governing international pesticide legislation is one of *caveat emptor* or 'let the buyer beware'. This should be replaced by a new recognition on the part of exporting nations of their responsibility as sellers. By subjecting exports to controls based on the need for consultation with importing countries, this responsibility can be fulfilled and safeguards exercised without infringing the sovereignty of the importing countries.

Following President Reagan's reversal of the Carter Executive Order in the US, the US agrochemical industry has proposed amendments to the FIFRA rules which would remove the present government to government communications and would do away with the notification requirement for pesticide intended for uses not registered in the US.[39] It is apparent, however, that not all US companies would adhere to this industry position. Velsicol, for example, "strongly supports the current regulations concerning pesticide exports".[40]

For the present though, according to Jacob Scherr of the Natural Resources Defense Council:

"The US, with existing export notice procedures for shipments of banned toxic chemicals, pesticides, consumer products, and hazardous wastes, is still way out in front of European and other exporting nations."[41]

The lead position of the US, he says, "is due in large measure to the concern and activities of non-governmental organisations here during the last decades".[42]

European Policy

In Europe the issue of hazardous exports is a relatively new one and there are currently no specific controls in Britain or in the EEC on the export of pesticides which are banned or severely restricted in their countries of origin. Already, though, OXFAM's approaches to the pesticide industry reveal that there is some agreement in principle to export legislation in Europe. Swiss company Ciba-Geigy, for example, have said that they

"would not oppose an export regulation similar to the one applied in the USA...We agree that government must ensure that potentially harmful agrochemicals who are unacceptable for domestic purposes in the exporting country are not permitted to be exported without the knowledge and consent of the appropriate authorities in the importing countries".[43]

The adoption of strict pesticide export controls in Europe would not only help to safeguard the health and environment of Third World countries directly, it would also increase the likelihood of further international controls and of action by other exporting countries. In addition, European countries would be acting upon the repeated resolutions of UNEP and fulfilling an obligation laid upon them by the resolution of the United Nations General Assembly referred to earlier. The UN resolution was passed in December 1979, yet a year later *International Agricultural Development* magazine was able to report that:

"European legislators seem even more reluctant than their American counterparts to take action to stop the export of dangerous chemicals. The European community, for instance, sees no point in setting up a notification system."[44]

In January 1980 an official of the UK Department of the Environment had this to say about notification regulations:

"As far as I am aware only the legislators in the USA have so far felt it necessary to impose this duty upon their administrations. You will find that the EEC Directive specifically excludes exports to 'Third countries' from the provisions of the Directive. This is not done out of malice. It is standard practice to spell out in this way the limitations of a Directive.

UK legislation does not presume to extend outside the UK and in general, we would expect other countries to adopt whatever legislative measures they felt were appropriate to their own needs."[45]

Yet there is no requirement that the UK exporters or Government give importing countries the information they need to make their decisions. While banned and restricted hazardous pesticides pose a threat to the health of Third World people, the EEC, exporter of nearly two-thirds of pesticides in world trade, and the UK, exporter of nearly an eighth, stand aside and adopt no relevant statutory provisions.

EEC Directive 67/548/EEC, as amended in September 1979 (known as the 'sixth amendment'), contains provisions for the classification, packaging and labelling of dangerous substances, and requires manufacturers to convey certain information to the authorities about any new substances they plan to place on the market.[46]

Directive 79/117/EEC prohibits the placing on the market in member countries of pesticides containing certain active ingredients, except for specified and very limited uses.[47] Neither of these directives includes specific provisions regarding the export of the substances covered. The latter directive specifically excludes export to third countries.

UK Policy

Apart from relevant EEC Directives there are three main controls exercised on pesticide use in Britain. The Pesticides Safety Precautions Scheme (PSPS) is a non-statutory agreement between the Government and manufacturers. Under this scheme, manufacturers have undertaken to notify the Ministry of Agriculture, Fisheries and Food before marketing any new pesticide or suggesting a new use of an existing one. The manufacturer provides data from which the Ministry decides how to proceed. The pesticide can proceed through four stages of clearance: trials clearance, limited clearance, provisional commercial clearance and commercial clearance. Before reaching a decision, the relevant department may seek advice from a scientific subcommittee. Draft recommendations then normally go to the Advisory Committees on Pesticides. This important Committee consists of government-appointed scientists and civil servants.

The results of the PSPS deliberations are recommendation sheets, describing uses of pesticides and necessary precautions and labelling requirements. The PSPS has no statutory authority and is not designed to give any protection to foreign importers or users. There is no statutory provision that the recommendation sheets or the data on which they are based be communicated to foreign purchasers, nor that their labelling requirements apply to products for export. The recommendation sheets give only the most basic information on how the product should be used in the UK. They do not include scientific data on the pesticide concerned. Nevertheless, these sheets do give a broad indication of hazard and state whether the pesticide is covered by Health and Safety Regulations. These sheets may be made available outside the UK on request and are currently received by about a dozen government departments in Third World countries.[48]

The Ministry of Agriculture also issue 'certificates of free sale' to exporters if these are requested by importing country governments. These certificates would confirm that the pesticide had been cleared under the PSPS, but would given no further information about the UK regulatory status of the pesticide or its potential hazard to man or the environment. The total number of certificates issued up to February 1982 stood in the region of 250, covering exports to some 20 Third World countries.[49]

Concerning the protection of users in the UK, the PSPS recommendations may advise that the use of a pesticide is so hazardous that it should be banned, that it should be regulated under the Health and Safety (Agriculture) (Poisonous Substances) Regulations, or that only voluntary precautions are necessary. These decisions have no repercussions for exports. Even if it is decided to ban the use of a pesticide in the UK it can still be exported, subject only to any restrictions on the part of the importing country, even if these are minimal or non-existent.

The second main control is the Health and Safety (Agriculture) (Poisonous Substances) Regulations, 1975. These statutory regulations classify the most hazardous pesticides into four classes and specify precautions to be taken in the use of each. The regulations include use of protective clothing, age limits, limits on hours of work and condition of apparatus. They require employers to keep a register of operations using these restricted substances. In addition, washing facilities must be provided. Again there is no statutory provision that any of this health and safety information be communicated to overseas purchasers, nor that any export should be prevented because these health and safety conditions could not be adhered to in the importing country.

The third main control on pesticides in Britain is through the Poisons Rules of 1978 and their accompanying Poisons List. The Poisons Rules govern sale, supply, labelling, packaging, storage and transport of listed poisons, including many pesticides. The rules restrict which persons may sell listed poisons. They require that some poisons be coloured, that containers be stout and impervious, and that they be labelled with strictly defined cautions and warnings. Poisons to be exported to purchasers outside the UK are exempted from these requirements.

Two other UK schemes are worth mentioning although neither covers pesticides for export. The Agricultural Chemicals Approval Scheme (ACAS) 'is a voluntary scheme under which efficacy of proprietary brands...can be officially approved" in order "to enable users to select, and advisors to recommend, efficient and appropriate crop protection chemicals and to discourage the use of unsatisfactory products".[50]

The British Agrochemical Supply Industry Scheme (BASIS) is a registration scheme for pesticide distributors set up by trade organisations. BASIS has defined minimum standards for storage premises, safety precautions and labelling and disposal of containers, and training standards for field, sales and technical staff.[51]

None of these controls on pesticides in the UK is intended to provide any statutory protection to foreign purchasers or users. Nor do they provide any obligation to exchange information with the importing country governments. The information exchange which occurs through the circulation of recommendation sheets and the provision of certificates of free sale, though it deserves some credit, provides only a minimal indication of the UK regulatory status of the pesticide and of precautions recommended in its use. Also, these measures are initiated only at the specific request of the importing country. There is no framework for consultation or exchange of more detailed data. There are no requirements regarding packaging, labelling or quality control for pesticides destined for export. There is no provision for an export to be stopped at the request of the recipient government, or for any consideration to be made of the costs and benefits likely to result for either country should the export take place.

If the UK Government were to take seriously the expressed wishes of Third World people and governments, and the resolutions of international organisations, it would have to adopt new legislation, or amend the existing measures, in order to control the export of hazardous pesticides effectively. It would also have to make positive efforts to encourage and support similar legislation in the EEC and other countries, as well as playing a positive role in any international initiatives, such as through OECD or the UN.

Export Control Proposals

Export control legislation should have four main goals[52]:

   to develop the capability of each nation to make its own decisions by providing the importing government with all available information and, where requested, with aid in the form of technical and administrative training;

— to protect foreign purchasers by ensuring full and honest labelling and promotion;

   to prohibit the export of certain products which are considered, after full consultation, to pose a substantial threat to health and environment, and

   to gather comprehensive information on the export of hazardous pesticides.

These goals would be achieved in the UK by legislation for the following controls:

1 *Export licensing:* All pesticides banned under the Pesticides Safety Precautions Scheme, covered by the Health and Safety (Agriculture) (Poisonous Substances) Regulations or the Poisons Rules, or restricted under any relevant EEC Directive, would be banned from export, unless an export licence were granted by the relevant authority. Such authority would probably represent both the Ministry of Agriculture and the Health and Safety Executive and its deliberations should be open to the evidence of the public and of non-governmental organisations. A licence would be granted only if the exporter were able satisfactorily to demonstrate that:

   a The exporter was complying with all relevant regulations, including labelling and packaging requirements.

   b The product met the requirements of the foreign purchaser, particularly with regard to quality.

   c The government of the importing country had been notified of the hazardous nature of the product and had requested that it be exported.

2 *Notification:* The importing country government would be notified before any export could be licensed. The notice would include details of the UK regulatory status of the pesticide and the reasons for such regulation, including relevant scientific data. The notice would also include information concerning possible substitutes for the hazardous chemical. Only if the importing country government, having received notification, requested the product, could a licence be granted. Secondly, any new regulatory actions would be routinely notified to foreign governments. Further details would be available on request. Such 'regulatory alerts' would be issued in summary

form at least on an annual basis.

3 *Packaging and Labelling:* All exported pesticides, whether restricted or not, would have to be safely packaged, and labelled in English and in the language of the country of destination, and use symbols as far as possible. Labels would include the generic name of the pesticide, directions for use, storage and disposal instructions, warnings of hazards to people and the environment and how to prevent them, symptoms of poisoning and first aid treatment, and a sell-by date. Pesticides banned for use in the UK would clearly state on the label that they are prohibited from use in the UK.

4 Any claims on labels or accompanying promotional material would be required not to be false or misleading.

These proposals represent a broad outline of the kind of measures which should be taken. The precise details would, of course, have to be drafted by the Government on the basis of appropriate consultations and expert advice. Exact requirements would have to be worked out, for example, on how to deal with different formulations of the same active ingredient; on renewal procedures for export licences, and on the need for confidentiality of some data.

Controls on exports of pesticides from the UK would require legislation and would undoubtedly result in some cost to the taxpayer, and this must of course be borne in mind in determining the exact measures to be taken. It must also be borne in mind, though, that the payment of this price could greatly assist health and food production in the Third World.

The basic framework of licensing and notification would give Third World countries the opportunity to exercise informed consent with respect to its import of the most hazardous pesticides. In the absence of such consent the shipment could be halted prior to export.

These measures, though, would only provide a basic statutory framework. Ideally, they should be supported by technical assistance which would enhance Third World countries' own ability to make regulations and to make effective use of the information exchanged. Such export legislation would not infringe the sovereignty of other nations. Rather, it would fulfil an obligation to co-operate constructively with other nations in the pursuit of safe and responsible trading practices. It would allow for differences in the needs of different countries but it would accept UK legislation as a starting point in determining the suitability of a pesticide for export. Providing the product was properly labelled and of good quality, then the power of decision would remain firmly with the importing country.

The UK would also be protecting its own consumers to some extent from residues in imported food of pesticides banned or restricted in the UK. A further advantage would accrue to the UK in terms of foreign policy. This latter issue has been an important factor in the US debate on hazardous export legislation and was recently expressed by the US Deputy Assistant Secretary of State for Oceans and International Environmental and Scientific Affairs:

> "Of central concern to the Department [of State], " she said, "are the potential adverse foreign relations consequences which might result from any damage to the public health and environment

abroad, traceable to hazardous substances and products exported from the United States."[53]

There may be some understandable concern in the UK that a reduction in pesticide exports could threaten jobs in the industry. The jobs threatened, however, would be in the production of banned or restricted pesticides which may themselves pose some degree of hazard to the UK workers. An indication of this potential hazard has been provided by the Kepone incident in the US. Kepone was an unregistered pesticide manufactured solely for export. In 1975 it was found that 70 people associated with the plant became seriously ill from Kepone exposure and the plant was closed.[54]

More importantly, though, it is not at all clear that pesticide export controls *would* lead to any loss of exports or of jobs — and they may do just the opposite. On the one hand, UK pesticide exports could fall if Third World importers decided to transfer their business to countries without export controls. If their purchasing decisions are based solely on price and convenience, they may take this action simply in order to avoid any extra bureaucracy. Such a loss in market share, though, may not actually reduce UK jobs or exports because it should be offset, to some degree, by the expected growth in the total Third World market.

Some actions could affect UK pesticide exports in either direction. UK export controls, by providing information and alerting Third World governments to the problems, may, for example, lead to better controls on the use of restricted pesticides in the Third World and/or the substitution of safer for more hazardous pesticides.

On the other hand, export controls could increase UK pesticide exports. Responsible Third World importers would be assured that a purchase from Britain would be properly packaged and labelled and of assured quality. This could act as a strong incentive to buy British.

In addition, technical assistance in support of export controls would help Third World governments to control imports more effectively and so prevent hazardous imports from non-regulating countries. Export controls should also be supported by strong efforts internationally to encourage other countries to adopt similar controls. If this proved successful any impact of export controls on trade would be only temporary. International activities to control the trade in pesticides and to improve their safety and efficacy in use, should be a high priority for the governments of pesticide-exporting countries.

Measures to exchange information and to make safer the world's trade in and use of pesticides should be the subject of urgent consideration by all international organisations. Strong and binding international codes of practice on the labelling and advertising of pesticides, for example, would greatly enhance the safety and efficacy of worldwide pesticide use. Such codes could be adopted through WHO, ILO, FAO and UNEP, with their respective responsibilities for health, labour, agriculture and the environment. All of these considerations are ultimately aimed at the maintenance and improvement of human health and so, perhaps, WHO would be the most appropriate lead agency. These international agencies can also play a major role in the implementation of better pest management practices, especially integrated pest management (FAO/UNEP), the improvement of workers' health as a component of primary health care (WHO), and the training of workers in the safe use of pesticides (ILO).

Some of these international actions have already begun and should be strongly supported, expanded and improved. For example, the OECD has discussed the development of an internationally consistent hazardous substances export policy.[55] The OECD has also recently set up an Expert Group on Information Exchange Related to Export of Hazardous Chemicals. This group held its first meeting in April 1981.[56] FAO and UNEP have set up a Global Medium Term Programme for the Development and Application of IPM. This should be stepped up and member governments should make available the necessary funds. WHO has set up a Medium Term Programme of Action on Workers' Health (1979-1984). ILO has published guidelines for the safe use of pesticides. WHO and FAO produce data sheets on some pesticides and lay down pesticide residue standards through the Codex Alimentarius Commission. UNEP has set up the International Register of Potentially Toxic Chemicals.

All of these programmes would be greatly assisted if pesticide exports were controlled and if pesticide advertising and promotion were subject to a strict code of practice. Irresponsible and misleading advertising and promotion exacerbates all the problems which these international programmes are trying to combat. WHO has had experience of devising and implementing a code of marketing practice for artificial baby-milk. It should work with non-governmental organisations and the pesticide industry towards the adoption of a code for pesticide marketing. This would greatly assist the work of other agencies, as well as its own programmes for workers' health, pesticide safe use and vector control. UN member governments should put forward official proposals to WHO to ensure that work can begin on a code at the earliest opportunity.

In looking at the problems associated with pesticide use, especially in the Third World, this book has also discussed the kind of policies which would help to solve these problems. In this chapter these policy issues have been dealt with in more detail, especially recommendations for UK export controls and an international advertising code of practice. There follows a summary of the action OXFAM would like to see taken. The recommendations to the governments of pesticide-exporting countries concentrate specifically in the UK, and the EEC. Nevertheless, it is important that all pesticide-exporting countries should adopt similar measures.

SUMMARY OF RECOMMENDATIONS

OXFAM strongly urges all the governments and agencies concerned to give full and serious consideration to these proposals, and to act upon them as soon as practically possible. Page numbers after each recommendation refer back to relevant sections of the text.

1 Third World Governments

1.1 Make efforts to develop the effective control of pesticide imports, and legislation on formulation, distribution, advertising, promotion and use of pesticides. (pp.53, 143.)

1.2 Examine the feasibility of joint initiatives by agricultural extension and primary health care services aimed at the effective prevention and treatment of pesticide poisoning. (pp.53, 129, 143.)

1.3 Improve agricultural extension services, especially regarding their capacity to implement IPM programmes geared to the needs of small and marginal farmers and landless labourers. (pp.53, 136, 141.)

2 The UK Government

2.1 Initiate an enquiry into the problems of pesticide exports and information exchange with a view to the introduction of appropriate legislation. (pp.62, 66, 153-9.)

2.2 Support and encourage international action, including a code of marketing practice. (pp.123, 158-9.)

2.3 Strengthen and improve the monitoring of pesticide residues in imported foodstuffs. (pp.59, 62.)

2.4 Give greater financial support to the positive activities of the Overseas Development Administration and other agencies in the provision of training and technical assistance for pesticide management and integrated pest management. (pp.75, 85, 141, 157.)

3 The EEC

3.1 Adopt pesticide export controls and notification procedures. (pp.62, 66, 153-4.)

4 WHO and FAO

4.1 Produce a model code of practice on pesticide usage (which should include advertising, promotion, labelling, packaging etc) and bring it to the attention of their member governments. (pp.53, 90, 123, 158-9.)

5 The Pesticide Industry

5.1 Adhere to all export control legislation and voluntary codes of practice. (p.142.)

5.2 Ensure that no pesticides are sold without full and accurate labelling in local languages, and symbols where possible, and appropriately sturdy packaging. (pp.53, 92.)

5.3 Ensure that all promotional and advertising material incorporates appropriate warnings and precautions and makes no false or misleading claim. (pp.25, 53, Ch.9.)

5.4 Investigate and review marketing practices, particularly the payment of commission to sales staff, in the light of the need for safe and effective pest management strategies in the Third World. (Ch.9.)

5.5 Increase efforts to develop selective pesticides and application equipment suitable for use in the context of IPM in Third World countries. (pp.128, 141.)

6   **Governmental and Non-governmental Development Agencies**

6.1 Adopt procedures to avoid simply funding pesticides and to encourage the implementation of IPM. (pp.75, 141.)

6.2 Increase support for training and technical assistance in support of any pesticide funding. (p.75.)

6.3 Work with international organisations to monitor advertising, labelling and pesticide use practices. (pp.123, 159.)

7   **Research Needs**

There are many areas where valuable research could be carried out or expanded. Such research can be carried out by governmental, non-governmental and international agencies and by the pesticide industry. Priority research areas include:

7.1 Pest resistance in plant breeding. (p.85.)

7.2 Development and implementation of IPM. (pp.137-9.)

7.3 Farmers' and farmworkers' perceptions of pests and pesticides. (p.5, 77.)

7.4 The incidence, prevention and treatment of pesticide poisoning. (Ch.4.)

7.5 The development of protective clothing and other equipment suitable for use under Third World conditions. (pp.39, 128.)

7.6 Use of symbols in pesticide labelling. (pp.90, 92.)

7.7 Development of selective pesticides. (p.128.)

These measures alone will not eradicate all pesticide-related problems, let alone solve the food and health problems of the poor. If adopted, though, they will make a significant positive contribution to safety, health, food supply and the environment. If they are not adopted, the future for many millions in the Third World could be one of the pesticide-induced agricultural crisis, epidemic pesticide poisoning and increasing incidence of malaria and vector-borne diseases. The smallest delay costs lives. All of us have a responsibility to exercise our energies towards the adoption of these recommendations. This may be the final chapter of a book, but for the campaign to eradicate the problems of pesticide use in the Third World it is just a beginning.

Notes and References

Introduction — Notes and References

(1)   Prem Chandran John, Deenabandu Medical Mission, Tamil Nadu, India, in interview with the author, 14 September 1980.

(2)   The World Bank, *World Development Report, 1980*, Washington DC, 1980, Table 19.

(3)   Ibid., p. 35.

(4)   ILO, "Making Work More Human: Working Conditions and Environment", offprint from the Report of the Director General to the International Labour Conference, 1975; ILO, Geneva, 1976.

(5)   WHO, *Workshop on Occupational Health Care in Agriculture*, Geneva, 1979, p. 3.

(6)   OECD, *Report of the Steering Committee on Pest Control Under the Conditions of Small Farmer Food Crop Production in Developing Countries*, Paris, 1977, pp. 15-16.

(7)   *North-South: A Programme for Survival* (The Brandt Report), Pan, London, 1980, p. 82. Other sources give different figures and these are discussed in more detail in footnote 5 of Chapter 3.

(8)   "Pesticides in Agriculture", Evidence to the Royal Commission on Environment Pollution from some members of staff of the Department of Zoology and Applied Entomology, Imperial College, London, p. 1.

(9)   Pimentel's studies are discussed in greater detail in Chapter 7. See, for example, D. Pimentel et al., "A Cost Benefit Analysis of Pesticide Use in US Food Production", in T.J. Sheets and David Pimentel (eds), *Pesticides: Their Contemporary Roles in Agriculture, Health and the Environment*, The Humana Press, Clifton, New Jersey, 1979.

(10) These and other examples can be found in Lim G.S. and S.H. Ong *Pesticide Benefits and Side Effects*, Southeast Asian Workshop on Pesticide Management, Bangkok, 1977.

A. Barr, C.S. Koehler and R.F. Smith, *Crop Losses — Rice: Field Losses to Insects, Diseases, Weeds, and Other Pests*, UC/AID, 1975. pp. 20-21.

(11) —   Lim and Ong, op. cit.

—   *Pesticides in the Modern World*, A Symposium prepared by members of the Co-operative Programme of Agro-Allied Industries with FAO and other United Nations Organisations, 1972, pp. 20-21.

(12) *Pesticides in the Modern World*, ibid., p. 1.

(13) USAID, *Environmental Impact Statement of the AID Pest Management Program*, Washington DC, 1977, Vol. 1. p. 176.

(14) A more detailed discussion of pesticides and their impact on malaria is the subject of Chapter 3.

(15) Lim and Ong, op. cit., p. 3.

(16) S. Patton, I. Craig and G.R. Conway, "The Pesticide Industry", in Gordon R. Conway (ed), *Pesticide Resistance and World Food Production*, Imperial College Centre for Environmental Technology, London, May 1980, p. 59. This source gives insecticide consumption as 35.5% of world pesticide consumption. It also shows (p. 58) that less developed countries consume 30% of all insecticides. Thus, insecticides used in the Third World account for 10.65% of world pesticide consumption. We estimate that the Third World uses approximately 15% of pesticides (see note 20) which means that insecticides account for more than two thirds of Third World pesticide use.

(17) The International Register of Potentially Toxic Chemicals of the UN Environment Programme, lists the synonyms of chemical names. For malathion, for example, 85 synonyms are listed.

(18) Allan Woodburn, Wood, Mackenzie & Co., in telephone interview with the author, 24 September 1981, confirmed in writing, 29 January 1982.

(19) David Pimentel, "Socio-economic Costs & Benefits of Pesticide Use", South-east Asian Workshop on Pesticide Management, Bangkok, 1977, p. 5.

(20) Figures vary between 10% and 21%. Pimentel, ibid., estimated nearly 21%. National Academy of Sciences, *Pest Control: An Assessment of Present and Alternative Tech-*

nologies: Vol. V: Pest Control and Public Health, Washington DC, 1976, p. 210, estimates 15–20%. D. Weir and M. Schapiro, *Circle of Poison*, Inst. for Food and Development Policy, San Francisco, 1981, p. 6, estimated 20%. Conway, op. cit., p. 58, however, gives a figure of only 10%. Our estimate is based on the assumptions that 97% of pesticides are manufactured outside the Third World, that Third World production is growing at the same rate as Third World imports, i.e. 15% (average from 1974 to 1977) (1978 UN Yearbook of International Trade Statistics) and that the conversion of $2 to £1 applies. These assumptions give 1978 Third World imports of $1,111,773,000 = £555,886,000, exports of $112,492,000 = £56,246,000 and production of £126 million (3% £4,200 million). This gives consumption of £625,640,000. With world consumption of £4,200 million, we have a Third World percentage of 14.9%. John T. Braunholtz, "Techno-economic considerations", *Chemistry and Industry* 17 November 1979, p. 789, quotes estimates that, at grower prices, "The world crop protection market has grown from £500M in 1960, £1,750M in 1970 to £4,200M in 1978". This gives an average growth rate of 12.5% per annum between 1960 and 1978. On the assumption of world growth of 12.5% per annum and Third World growth by 15% per annum, the Third World share would increase to 15.6% by 1980, and 16.3% by 1982.

(21) Patton, Craig and Conway, op. cit., p. 58.

(22) 1978 UN Yearbook of International Trade Statistics, p. 312.

(23) UN Commodity Trade Statistics 1978. These dollar values have been converted to sterling at a rate calculated by dividing dollar values per tonne from US statistics by sterling values per tonne from UK export statistics (Business Monitor PQ279.4). More complete figures appear in Appendix 2, Table 3, which also gives the exchange rates used.

(24) UN Yearbook, op. cit.

(25) Based on figures from the UN 1978 Yearbook of International Trade Statistics, p. 312. In thousands of US dollars, the figures for 1978 are as follows:

US: 447,939

EEC (9) :	1,675,325
Switz. :	273,415
Sweden :	7,059
Greece :	11,546
Spain :	12,538
Norway :	3,597

W. Eur, excluding Portugal, Austria, and Finland : 1,983,480

1,983,480 divided by 447,939 equals 4.428

Chapter 1 — Notes and References

(1) *New Internationalist,* November 1979. Washington Post, 25 February 1980.

(2) In response to an OXFAM questionnaire sent to agricultural specialists, new pest outbreaks were reported by 14 respondents from 10 Third World countries.

(3) R. van den Bosch, *The Pesticide Conspiracy,* Prism Press, 1980, p.22.

(4) Paul DeBach, *Biological Control by Natural Enemies,* Cambridge University Press, 1974 pp. 2-3.

(5) Letter from Deanna Donovan to Inst. of Current World Affairs, dated 18 October 1979.

(6) Ray F. Smith, "The Role of Pesticides in the Concept of Pest Management", S.E. Asian Workshop of Pesticide Management, Bangkok, 1977.

(7) *OECD Report of the Steering Group on Pest Control under the Conditions of Small Farmer Food Crop Production in Developing Countries,* OECD Planning Group on Science & Technology for Developing Countries, OECD, Paris, 1977, p.30. (This extremely valuable study was funded by the British Aid Programme.)

(8) See Chapter 2, particularly the sections on Nicaragua and the Sudan.

(9) ICAITI, *An Environmental and Economic Study of the Consequences of Pesticide*

Use in Central American Cotton Production, Final Report, 2nd edition, ICAITI, Guatemala, 1977, pp.27-30. ICAITI is the Central American Research Institute for Industry. This study was carried out with assistance of members of the US National Academy of Sciences and was funded by the UN Environment Programme.

(10)   Margi Bryant, "The Gezira Scheme: A Lost Cause?" Earthscan, London, (mimeo) 1980. *Integrated Pest Control: Report of the Ninth Session of the FAO/UNEP Panel of Experts held in Wad Medani, the Sudan 9-13 December, 1979,* FAO Rome, 1980.

(11)   J.P. Kulshrestha, "Integrated Management of Rice Insect Pests" (mimeo).

(12)   *The Star* (Malaysia), 9 June 1979. Figures in sterling are converted from Malaysian dollars at a rate of £1=$(M)4.5.

(13)   Dr. J. Jeyeratnam, "Planning for the Health of the Worker", SLAAS Theme Seminar, Colombo, 1979.

(14)   Percy Abeywardena, Deputy Director of Extension Services, in interview with the author, 8 September 1980. Also A. Nanayakkara, Sales Manager, Lankem (Ceylon) Ltd, 3 September 1980.

(15)   In interview with the author, 5 September 1980.

(16)   OXFAM project file, SL 12, "Planthopper Control Research".

(17)   In interview with the author, 10 September 1980.

(18)   *Plant Protection Problems in South-east Asia,* report by East Asian Management Study Team, 1971, p.9. This study was conducted by Cornell University.

(19)   Ray F. Smith, "Integrated Control and Its Practical Implementation", in *The Agromedical Approach to Pesticide Management,* UC/AID, 1976, pp.13-23.

Chapter 2 – Notes and References

(1)   –   Ray F. Smith, "Resistance to Pesticides as a World Problem in Pest Control" in *A Report on Seminar Workshop and Training in Pesticide Management, Indonesia* UC/AID, 1974, p.238.

    –   H.T. Reynolds, "Problems of Resistance in Pests of Field Crops", *Proc. XV International Congress of Entomology,* Washington DC, 1976, pp.796-7.

    –   Robert van den Bosch, *The Pesticide Conspiracy,* Prism Press, Dorchester, Dorset, 1980, pp.42-3.

    –   David Pimentel et al, "Environmental and Social Costs of Pesticides: a preliminary assessment", *OIKOS* 34:2 (1980), Copenhagen, p.131.

    –   I. Craig, G.R. Conway and G.A. Norton, "The Consequences of Resistance" in Gordon R. Conway (ed), *Pesticide Resistance and World Food Production,* Imperial College Centre for Environmental Technology, University of London, 1980, p.52.

(2)   Robert van den Bosch, op. cit., p.21.

(3)   S. Patton and G.R. Conway, "Fungicide and Bactericide Resistance" in Conway (ed), op. cit., p.29.

(4)   I. Craig, "Herbicide Resistance", in Conway (ed), op.cit., p.35.

(5)   –   Smith, op. cit., p.239.

    –   *Business Times* (Malaysia), 17 June 1979, reporting on UNEP annual report.

(6)   –   FAO, *Pest Resistance to Pesticides, and Crop Loss Assessment – 2,* Rome 1979, Appendices A & B.

    –   FAO, *Pest Resistance to Pesticides and Crop Loss Assessment – 3,* report of the 2nd session of the FAO panel of experts, FAO, Rome 1981, Appendices A & B.

    –   G.P. Georghiou and C.E. Taylor, "Pesticide Resistance as an Evolutionary Phenomenon" in *Proc. of XV International Congress of Entomology,* Washington DC, 1976.

    –   An 'arthropod' is an "animal of phylum Arthropoda with segmented body and jointed limbs, e.g. insect, spider, crustacean" (Concise Oxford Dictionary).

(7)   Smith, op. cit., p. 239.

(8)   Georghiou and Taylor, op. cit., p.762.

(9)   Dr. R.M. Sawicki, "Resistance of Insects to Insecticides", *Span* 22,2, 1979, p.51.

(10) A.W.A. Brown, "Epilogue: Resistance as a Factor in Pesticide Management" *Proc. of XV International Congress of Entomology,* Washington DC, 1976, pp.817-818.

(11) Conway (ed), op. cit., p.3. para.17..

(12) Reynolds, op. cit., p.794.

(13) — Smith, op. cit., p.243.
      — Sawicki, op. cit., p.52.

(14) — G.R. Conway, "The Future" in Conway (ed) op. cit., pp.77-78.
      — Peter A.C. Ooi and K.I. Sudderuddin, "Control of Diamond-back Moth in the Cameron Highlands, Malaysia", *Proc. MAPPS Pl. Prot. Confr.,* Kuala Lumpur, 1978.
      — K.I. Sudderuddin and Kok Pooi-Fong, "Insecticide Resistance in Plutella xylos tella collected from the Cameron Highlands of Malaysia" *FAO Plant Protection Bulletin,* Vol. 26, No. 2, 1978, pp.53-57.
      — Dr. Ishmael Sudderuddin, Univ. of Malaysia, in interview with the author 23 September 1980.

(15) Conway (ed) op. cit., p.78.

(16) Brown, op. cit., p.816.

(17) D. F. Waterhouse, "FAO Activities in the Field of Pesticide Resistance" *Proc. of XV International Congress of Entomology,* 1976, p.788.

(18) Sawicki, op. cit., p.50.

(19) *Pesticides in Agriculture,* Evidence to the Royal Commission on Environmental Pollution from some members of the staff of the Dept. of Zoology and Applied Entomology, Imperial College, London, p.3.

(20) M.J. Way "Integrated control — practical realities", *Outlook on Agriculture,* Vol. 9, No. 3, 1977.

(21) Pimentel, et al, *OIKOS,* 1980, op. cit., p.131.

(22) Nigel Pollard, "The Gezira Scheme — A Study in Failure", *The Ecologist,* Vol. II. No. 1, Jan/Feb. 1981, pp.21-32.

(23) Margi Bryant, "The Gezira Scheme: a lost cause?", Earthscan, London, 1980.

(24) Pollard, op. cit., p.25.

(25) FAO, *Integrated Pest Control,* Report of the Ninth Session of the FAO/UNEP Panel of Experts held in Wad Medani, the Sudan, 9-13 December 1979, p.1.

(26) Ibid., pp.10-12 and 46-51. The quotations appear on pages 10 and 12 respectively.

(27) Mario A. Vaughan & Gladys Leon Q., "Pesticide Management on a Major Crop with Severe Resistance Problems", *Proc. XV Int. Congress of Entomology,* Washington DC, 1976, pp.812-815.

(28) Ibid., p.812.

(29) Ibid.

(30) FAO, *The Development and Application of Integrated Pest Control in Agriculture:* Formulation of a Co-operative Global Programme. Report on an ad hoc session of the FAO Panel of Experts on Integrated Pest Control held in Rome, 15-25 Oct. 1974, FAO, 1975, Appendix B, p.2. This appendix summarised the Nicaraguan case and the solutions attempted. We will examine the incidence of pesticide poisoning in greater detail in Chapter 4.

(31) Georganne Chapin and Robert Wasserstrom, "Agricultural Production and Malaria Resurgence in Central America and India", *Nature,* Vol 293, 17 September 1981, Table 1, p.181.
      The impact of agricultural pesticide use on malaria is the subject of Chapter 3.

(32) Vaughan and Leon Q., op. cit., p.813.

(33) In interview with the author, 19 September 1980.

(34) Conway (ed), op. cit., p.4.

(35) Ibid., p.78.

(36) Reynolds, op. cit., p.798.

(37) G.R. Conway, "The Future", in Conway (ed), op. cit., pp.78-80.

(38) One example is the African mosquito, *Anopheles gambiae,* resistant to cyclodiene pesticides prior to their introduction in West Africa. (Sawicki, op. cit., p.51).

(39) John R. Corbett, "Technical considerations affecting the discovery of new pesti-cides", *Chemistry and Industry,* 17 November 1979, p.772.
(40) Ibid.
(41) S. Patton, I. Craig & G.R. Conway, "The Pesticide Industry", in Conway (ed), op. cit., p.71.
(42) Ibid., p.72.
(43) Ibid.
(44) Reynolds, op. cit., p.797.
(45) Detailed discussion of pesticide promotion in the Third World appears in Chapter 9.
(46) Joyce Tait, "Approaches to Pest Control in Developed and Developing Countries", *African Research and Documentation,* No. 20, 1979.
(47) FAO, *Model Extension Leaflet on Pest Resistance to Pesticides,* FAO, Rome, 1971.
(48) Conway (ed), op. cit., p.5.
(49) Sawicki, op. cit., p.52.
(50) The potential of the IPM strategy for the small farmer in the Third World will be discussed in Chapter 10.

Chapter 3 — Notes and References

(1) Richard Van Gelder, "Malaria Safari".
(2) USAID, *Environmental Impact Statement on the AID Pest Management Programme,* USAID, Washington DC, 1977, gives two conflicting figures. On p.196, Vol. 1, it says: "the global incidence of malaria is now about 120 million cases annually, of which nearly 100 million are in tropical Africa". On p.173, Vol. 2 it says: "the Director General of WHO estimated that there are over 200 million cases of malaria in Africa every year".

   OECD, *Report of the Steering Group on Pest Control Under the Conditions of Small Farmer Food Crop Production in Developing Countries,* OECD, Paris, p.19, gives "300 million cases and 3 million deaths per year".

   WHO, *Tropical Diseases,* p.7 describes malaria as "one of the most widespread diseases in the world, affecting some 200 million people".
(3) C.P. Pant & N.G. Gratz, "Malaria and Agricultural Development", *Outlook on Agriculture,* Vol. 10, No. 3, 1979, p.111: "According to a recent estimate by the World Health Organisation, the total number of malaria cases reported throughout the world was approximately 6,504,000 in 1977 (excluding China and Democratic Kampuchea)".
(4) USAID, op. cit., Vol. 2, p.173; Paul Harrison, *Inside the Third World,* Penguin, London, 1979, p.285.
(5) *North-South: A Programme for Survival* ("The Brandt Report"), Pan, London, 1980, p.82. Other figures are variable, for example WHO, *Resistance of Vectors and Reservoirs of Disease to Pesticides,* 22nd Report of the WHO Expert Committee on Insecticides, WHO, Geneva, 1976, gives 870,671,000 in malarious areas in 14 countries in 1974, p.34. Harrison, op. cit., says: "600 million people live in endemic areas in 60 countries", p.285. On the other hand Pant & Gratz, op cit., say, for 1976, that "89 countries or areas comprising 1,500 million people were still at moderate to high risk", p.111. "The World Bank Health Sector Policy Paper", Washington DC, Feb. 1980, says that "850 million live in areas where malaria continues to be transmitted despite activities to control it, while a further 345 million live in areas with little or no control efforts", p.14.
(6) George P. Georghiou, "Studies in Resistance to Carbamate and Organophosphorous Insecticides in Anopheles albimanus", *American Journal of Tropical Medicine and Hygiene,* Vol. 21, No. 5, 1972.
(7) Harrison, op. cit., p.285.
   Leslie Tuttle, *Draft Briefing on Malaria,* OXFAM America.
   Van Gelder, op. cit.
(8) USAID, op. cit., Vol. 2, p.156.
(9) Pant & Gratz, op. cit., p.113.

(10) Georganne Chapin & Robert Wasserstrom, "Agricultural Production and Malaria Resurgence in Central America and India", *Nature,* Vol. 293, 17 September 1981, p.181.

(11) Van Gelder, op. cit.

(12) E.B. Worthington, "Some Ecological Problems Concerning Engineering and Tropical Diseases", *Prog. Wat. Tech.* Vol. 11, Nos. 1/2, 1978, p.9.

(13) G. Melvyn Howe, *Man, Environment and Disease in Britain,* Penguin, London, 1972, pp.63-4.

(14) USAID, op. cit., Vol. 1, p.175.

(15) Pant and Gratz, op. cit., p.113.

(16) Harry Cleaver, "Malaria and the Political Economy of Public Health", *International Journal of Health Services,* Vol. 7, No. 4, 1977.

(17) USAID, op. cit., Vol. 1, p.176.

(18) Pant & Gratz, op. cit., p.113.

(19) Dr. Rahman (Regional Director for Health, Karnataka) and Mr. C.P. Vijayan (Assistant Director of Entomology, Communicable Disease Programme, Karnataka) in interview with the author, 19 September 1980.

(20) TAMS (Tippett, Abbett, McCarthy, Stratton) report, "Environmental Assessment: Accelerated Mahaweli Development Program", Volume IV (Human Environment), New York, 1980, (Assessment carried out for the Ministry of Mahaweli Development, Sri Lanka). Table K-3, p.K-8. USAID, op. cit., Vol. 1, p.178.

(21) Harry Cleaver, op. cit., p.559; USAID, op. cit., Vol. 2, p.150.

(22) WHO, *Tropical Diseases,* WHO/UNDP, Geneva, p.4.

(23) USAID, op. cit., Vol. 2, p.150.

(24) WHO, *World Health Statistical Annual,* Geneva, 1966-79, quoted in Chapin and Wasserstrom, op. cit., p.23, Table 1, p.181.

(25) World Bank, *Health Sector Policy Paper,* 1980, pp.14 and 54.

(26) USAID, op. cit., Vol. 2, p.178.

(27) TAMS report, op. cit.

(28) WHO, *Resistance of Vectors of Disease to Pesticides: Fifth Report of the WHO Expert Committee on Vector Biology and Control,* Technical Report Series 655, WHO, Geneva, 1980, p.70. *Anopheles albimanus* has developed resistance in Central America to DDT, dieldrin, HCH, malathion, fenitrothion, parathion methyl, jodfenphos, chlorpyrifos, chlorphoxim, phoxim, parathion and propoxur.

(29) DDT spraying began in 1946 and was reduced in 1964 after the very low malaria incidence of 1963. An intensified attack recommenced in 1968, but DDT resistance was evident from 1962 and of increasing operational significance from 1968 onwards. Malathion was first used in 1970 and became the principal insecticide after March 1975. An Intensive Malaria Control Programme commenced in 1976 with assistance from the UK, Netherlands and USA. The major recovery occurred from 1977 onwards.
  — TAMS report, op. cit., passim.
  — Tuttle, op. cit., pp.15-17.
  — WHO, *Resistance of the Vectors and Reservoirs of Disease to Pesticides,* 22nd Report of the WHO Expert Committee on Insecticides; Technical Report Series 585, WHO, Geneva, 1976, p.32.
  — OXFAM America, "A Popular Approach to Malaria Control in Sri Lanka: Preliminary Discussion" 17 February 1981, pp.8-9.

(30) USAID, op. cit., Vol. 2, pp.152-3.

(31) Nigel Pollard, "The Gezira Scheme -- A Study in Failure", *The Ecologist,* Vol. II, No. 1, Jan/Feb 1981, p.26.

(32) The Hindu, 13 September 1980, reporting on a lecture by Dr. V. Ramalingaswami, Director General of the Indian Council for Medical Research.

(33) Dr. Vijayama Thomas, University of Malaya, (Vice-Chairman of the WHO Expert Committee on Insecticides in 1975), in interview with the author, 23 September 1980. (Confirmed in writing 28 January 1982).

(34) WHO, *"Resistance of Vectors and Reservoirs of Disease to Pesticides,"* 22nd Report of the WHO Expert Committee on Insecticides, Technical Report Series 585, WHO, Geneva, 1976, p.26.

(35) R. Pal (WHO), "Problems of Insecticide Resistance in Insect Vectors of Human Disease", *XVth International Congress of Entomology*, Washington DC, 1976, p.800.

(36) FAO, *Pest Resistance to Pesticides and Crop Loss Assessment — 3*, report of the 2nd session of the FAO panel of experts, FAO, Rome, 1981, Appendix A.

(37) WHO, 22nd Report, 1976, op. cit., pp.10-15 and 34-35. WHO, 5th Report 1980, op. cit., p.9 and Annex 1, pp.69-79.

(38) Ibid., p.33; Pant & Gratz, op. cit., p.114; L.S. Self, "Pesticides in Modern Vector Control Practice", in *A Report on Seminar Workshop & Training in Pesticide Management*, UC/AID, Indonesia, 1974, p.143; USAID, op. cit., Vol. 1, p.192.

(39) ICAITI, *An Environmental and Economic Study of the Consequences of Pesticide Use in Central American Cotton Production*, Final Report, 2nd edition, Guatemala, 1977, p.150.

(40) WHO, 5th Report, 1980, op. cit., p.15.

(41) In interview with the author, 10 July 1980.

(42) Around 1970, for example, only 15-20% of DDT used was for public health purposes (USAID, op. cit., Vol. 1, p.179).
J.F. Copplestone, "A Global View of Pesticide Safety" in D.L. Watson and A.W.A. Brown (eds), *Pesticide Management and Insecticide Resistance* Academic Press, 1977, p.148, estimates 10% of pesticide production is used in Public Health programmes.

(43) WHO, 22nd Report, op. cit., p.21.

(44) George P. Georghiou, "The Implication of Agricultural Insecticides in the Development of Resistance by Mosquitoes", in *The Agromedical Approach to Pesticide Management*, UC/AID, 1976, p.25.

(45) ICAITI, op. cit., p.150.

(46) Ibid., pp.126-7.

(47) USAID, op. cit., vol. 1, p.180.

(48) David Werner, personal communication, 22 June 1981.

(49) See Chapter 4.

(50) WHO, *Safe Use of Pesticides*, 3rd Report of the WHO Expert Committee on Vector Biology and Control, Technical Report Series 634, WHO, Geneva, 1979, pp.17-18.

(51) A.T. Arayaratne, A.N.A. Abeyesundere & Michael F. Scott, "A Popular Approach to Malaria Control in Sri Lanka: Preliminary Discussion", OXFAM America, Boston, 1981.

(52) Tuttle, op. cit., p.10.

(53) Pant & Gratz, op. cit., p.115.

(54) Vector Control Research Centre, Pondicherry, Annual Report, 1980, p.6.

(55) WHO, 22nd Report, op. cit., p.77.

Chapter 4 — Notes and References

(1) — *Guardian*, Third World Review, 31 March 1980.
— ICAITI, *An Environmental and Economic Study of the Consequences of Pesticide Use in Central American Cotton Production: Final Report* 2nd edition, 1977, pp. 199-200.
— *New York Times*, 9 November 1977.

(2) John E. Davies, *Pesticides and the Environment: A Review of the Changing Profile of Human Health Effects*, V Inter-American Meeting on Foot and Mouth Disease and Zoonoses Control, World Health Organisation, Mexico City, 1972.

(3) WHO/FAO Data Sheets on Pesticides No. 6, 1975, "Parathion".

(4) WHO, *Safe Use of Pesticides*, 20th Report of the WHO Expert Committee on Insecticides, Tech. Rept. Series No. 513, Geneva, 1973.

(5) J. F. Copplestone, "A Global View of Pesticide Safety" in D.L. Watson and A.W.A. Brown (eds), *Pesticide Management and Insecticide Resistance*, Academic Press, 1977, pp. 147-155.

(6) J.F. Copplestone, Chief, Pesticide Development and Safe Use, WHO, in an interview with the author, 11 July 1980.

(7)   The total is 500,000 and 50% are in developed and 50% in developing countries. The death rate in developed countries (those where medical treatment and antidotes are readily available) is 1%. The total number of deaths is 9,200. This gives the following results:
        Developed countries — cases: 250,000; deaths: 2,500 (1%)
        Developing countries — cases: 250,000; deaths: 6,700 (9,200 minus 2,500)
        6,700 deaths out of 250,000 cases is a rate of 2.68%
        6,700 deaths out of a total of 9,200 is equal to 72.8% of the deaths.

(8)   Allan Woodburn, Wood, Mackenzie and Co. Agrochemical Service, in telephone interview with the author 24 September 1981.

(9)   On the basis of the limits of error at the time, the current estimate for the Third World could be as low as 187,000 with 5,025 deaths, or as high as 1,089,750 with 29,205 deaths.

(10) J.F. Copplestone, personal communication, 2 September 1981.

(11) J.F. Copplestone, 1977, op. cit., p. 153.

(12) ILO, *Guide to Health and Hygiene in Agricultural Work*, Geneva, 1979, p. 94.

(13) J.A.R. Bates, (Pesticide Residues Specialist, Plant Protection Service, FAO), *Pesticides — Constraints and Controls in Importing Countries*, paper to be presented at International Seminar on Controls of Chemicals in Importing Countries, Dubrovnik, 22–24 April 1981, p. 14.

(14) WHO,"Guidelines to the Use of the WHO Recommended Classification of Pesticides by Hazard", Geneva, May 1979.
For the purpose of this classification, hazard is defined as "the acute risk to health ... that might be encountered accidentally by any person handling the product in accordance with the directions". This takes account of both oral and dermal toxicities and the classification· may be adjusted if the "actual hazard to man differs from that indicated by LD_{50} assessments alone". p. 18.

(15) J.E. Davies, "Current Medical Problems of Pesticide Management" and "Medical Aspects of Pesticide Poisoning: Diagnosis and Treatment" in *The Agromedical Approach to Pesticide Management*, UC/AID, 1976, pp. 42 & 55.

(16) Esther Peterson and Robert Harris, *Background Report on the Executive Order on Federal Policy Regarding the Export of Banned or Significantly Restricted Substances*, The White House, Jan. 1981, p. 7.

(17) Dr. A.H. El-Sebae, "Incidents of Local Pesticide Hazards and their Toxicological Interpretation", in *Proceedings of the UC/AID-Univ. of Alexandria Seminar Workshop in Pesticide Management, 1977*, p. 145.

(18) — David Weir and Mark Schapiro, *Circle of Poison*, Institute for Food and Development Policy, San Francisco, 1981, pp. 23–4.
      — "Restricted Pesticides in the Philippines", Fertilizer and Pesticide Authority, Manila, revised Oct. 1980.
      — Florita E. Kentish and Dalton B. McKay, "Pest and Pesticide Management — Antigua", in E.G.B. Gooding (ed), *Pest and Pesticide Management in the Caribbean*, procs. of seminar and workshop 3–7 Nov. 1980, Vol. III, Consortium for International Crop Protection, pp. 12–20.

(19) Richard F. Blewitt, Vice President — Corporate Affairs, Velsicol Chemical Corporation, personal communication, 14 December 1981.
This letter was in reply to the author's letter to Velsicol's UK office dated 2 September 1981. The latter did not include the issue of Phosvel's availability in Antigua which did not come to the author's notice until March 1982.

(20) The labelling and promotion of pesticides in the Third World are dealt with in more depth in Chapter 9.

(21) ICAITI, op. cit., pp. 97–98.

(22) *New York Times*, 9 November 1977.

(23) "Management of Pesticides and Protection of the Environment", a report on a Seminar, UC/AID, San Salvador (mimeo), 1973, pp. 3–4.

(24) ICAITI, op. cit., p. 195.

(25) Ibid., pp. 88–91.

(26) Ibid., p. 196.

(27) Ibid., p. 195.

(28)   Ibid., p. 193.

(29)   Questionnaire response from an agronomist working in Guatemala.

(30)   *The Ecologist*, March 1980, p. 96.

(31)   Patrick J. O'Mahoney, *Multinationals and Human Rights*, Mayhew McCrimmon, Gt. Wakering, Essex, 1980, p. 283.

(32)   R.R. Najera and E. Sanchez de la Fuente, "Intoxicacion por plaguicidas en la comarca lagunera durante el ciclo agricola de 1974", *Salud Publica de Mexico*, Mexico DF, Mexico, Sept.–Oct. 1975, vol. 17, No. 5, pp. 687–698.

(33)   J. Jeyeratnam, Faculty of Medicine, Colombo, in interview with the author, 1 September 1980.

(34)   US figures indicate about 6,000 hospital admissions a year and 200 deaths. D. Pimentel, *Socioeconomic Costs and Benefits of Pesticide Use*, Southeast Asian Workshop on Pesticide Management, Bangkok, 1977. D. Pimentel, "Environmental and Social Costs of Pesticides: a preliminary assessment", *Oikos*, 34: 124–40, Copenhagen, 1980.

(35)   J. Jeyeratnam, *Planning for the Health of the Worker*, SLAAS, Theme Seminar, Annual Session, 1979.

(36)   J. Jeyeratnam, "Follow-up Study of 23 Cases of Pesticide Poisoning Admitted to a Government Hospital in Sri Lanka", (mimeo).

(37)   Ibid.

(38)   This account of the Endrex case is based on an interview with Mr B.N.Fox and Dr. R. Tincknell of Shell International Chemical Company, London, 17 November 1981, and on a letter from B.N. Fox of 23 April 1982. A written summary of the November meeting was sent to Shell by the author dated 21 December 1981. Shell had not queried the accuracy of this account at time of going to press.

(39)   The human nervous system has a chemical transmitter called acetylcholine which permits impulses to pass between nerves. When it has done its job it is destroyed by an enzyme called cholinesterase. This prevents the accumulation of acetylcholine which would cause continuous, uncontrolled nerve impulses resulting in tremors, convulsions and death. Organophosphorous pesticides act by destroying the protective enzyme cholinesterase, leading to a dangerous build-up of acetylcholine.

Repeated exposures to OPs can lower the cholinesterase level to the point where a relatively small additional exposure can produce symptoms of acute poisoning. Measurement of cholinesterase levels, therefore, provides an indication of the effects of OPs on exposed workers. Ideally, all workers should be examined periodically for this — they could then be withdrawn from further exposure and acute effects prevented.

(40)   ILO/PIACT National Tripartite Seminar on the Improvement of Working Conditions and Environment, "Situation Paper: Chemical Industries", Colombo, 1980.

(41)   B. Fox and R. Tincknell, Shell International Chemical Company, London, in interview with the author, 17 November 1981.

(42)   B. W. Cox, Manager, Publicity Department, ICI Ltd., Plant Protection Division, personal communication, 23 October 1981.

(43)   Werner Gebauer, Bayer, personal communication, 11 February 1982.

(44)   OXFAM project file, SL12.

(45)   "Formulary of Agro-Chemicals — 1979", List 1, Dept. of Govt. Printing, Sri Lanka, 1979.

(46)   —   "Promoting Safer Pest Control through Pesticide Retailers," UN Press Release No. G/100/81, through UN Information Service, Bangkok, Thailand.
       —   ESCAP Agricultural Information Development Bulletin, Vol. 3, No. 2, pp. 23–26.

(47)   Mr. Percy Abeywardena, Deputy Director of Extension Services, Kandy, Sri Lanka, in interview with the author, 8 September 1980.

(48)   A. Balasubramaniam, "Pesticides Act, 1974", Consumers Association of Penang Seminar on Health, Food and Nutrition, Sept. 1979.

(49)   —   Martin Kohr, CAP, in interview with the author, September 1980.
       —   *Star* (Malaysia), 18 April 1979.

(50)   Sahabat Alam Malaysia, *Pesticide Problems in a Developing Country*, SAM, Penang, 1981, p. 8.

(51)   *Utusan Konsumer*, April 1981, p. 9.

(52)   de B. Ashworth and A. Balasubramaniam, *Crop Protection in Malaysia*. A short version was presented to the Collaborative Pesticides Analytical Council's (CIPAC) Symposium at Oerias, Portugal, June 1975, p. 18.

(53)   Wong Kien Keong, Acting Dean, Department of Environmental Sciences, Universiti Pertanian Malaysia, Serdang, Selangor, "Impact of Pesticide Usage — A Case Study of Organchlorine Compound Levels in the Blood Serum of Selected Malaysian Population Groups", Seminar on Economics, Development and the Consumer, Nov. 1980, Consumers Association of Penang, Penang.

(54)   –   A. Balasubramaniam, *Price List of Pesticides Available in Peninsular Malaysia*, Division of Agriculture, Min. of Agriculture, Malaysia, 1980.
       –   EEC Directive 79/117/EEC, *Official Journal of the European Communities* Vol. 22, L33, 8 February 1979.
       –   WHO op. cit., (see ref. 14).
       –   *Approved Chemicals for Farmers and Growers, 1981*, Agricultural Chemicals Approvals Scheme, MAFF, HMSO, London, 1981.
       –   Ministry of Agriculture Fisheries and Food, "Chemical Compounds Used as Pesticides: Recommendations for Safe Use in the United Kingdom", London.

(55)   –   A. Balasubramaniam, *Status of Pesticides Usage and Their Control in Peninsular Malaysia*, Southeast Asian Workshop on Pesticide Management, Bangkok, 1977.
       –   Balasubramaniam, *Pesticides Act, 1974*, op. cit.
       –   The [Malaysia] Pesticides Act, 1974.
       –   Balasubramaniam, Secretary, Pesticides Board, Department of Agriculture, in interview with author, 23 September 1980.

(56)   *New Straits Times*, 22 July 1981.

(57)   Wongpanich, Kritalugsana and Deema, "Survey of Pesticide Hazards in Thailand".

(58)   Banpot Napompeth, "Mismanagement of Pesticides in Pest Control" in Philip S. Motooka (ed), *Procs. of Pest Management Seminar For Agricultural Administrators*, East–West Food Institute, East–West Center, Hawaii, 1974, p. 19.

(59)   Banpot Napompeth, "Thailand: National Profile on Pest Management and Related Problems", (mimeo) 1980, p. 25.

(60)   Personal communication, 10 August 1981.

(61)   Napompeth, 1980, op. cit., pp. 24–28.

(62)   Ibid., p. 24.

(63)   Ibid., p. 25.
       Banpot Napompeth, "Feasibility Study and Implementation of Soybean Pest Management Program in Thailand" in Philip S. Motooka (ed), *Procs. Planning Workshop on Co-operative Field Research in Pest Management*, East–West Food Institute, East–West Center, Hawaii, 1975, p. 15.

(64)   Wongpanich et al. op. cit., p. 187.

(65)   Banpot Napompeth, "Impact of Pesticide Laws in Thailand", in Philip Motooka (ed), *Procs. Conf. on the Impact of Pesticide Laws*, East–West Center, Hawaii, Dec. 1976, p. 52.

(66)   Napompeth, 1974, op. cit., p. 16.

(67)   John E. Davies, "Problems of Poisoning" in UC/AID, *A Report on Seminar Workshop and Training in Pesticide Management*, Jakarta, Indonesia, 1974, (UC/AID), p. 118.

(68)   J.E. Davies, R.F. Smith, V. Freed and S.A. Poznanski, "An Agromedical Approach to Pesticide Management", in ibid., pp. 287–8.

(69)   Dr. I. Darmansjah, "Medical Aspects of Pesticide Poisoning", in ibid., p. 171.

(70)   OXFAM project file, IND 55.

(71)   Consumer Currents, No. 37, May–June 1981, extracted from *Warta Konsumen* (Indonesia), January 1981.

(72)   R.T. Deang, "International Exchange of Regulatory Expertise" in *Proceedings of the US Strategy Conference on Pesticide Management*, Washington DC, 1979, p. 44.

(73)   Ms Melot Balisalisa, Pesticides Study Co-ordinator, Farmers Assistance Board Inc., Quezon City, Philippines, personal communication, 1981.

(74)   Francis C. Neri, Chief Information Officer, Fertiliser and Pesticide Authority , "The

Fertiliser and Pesticide Authority: An Overview of Thrusts and Policies", 28 February 1980, (mimeo), p. 3.

(75) Grace Goodell, *Consequences of the New HYV Technology*, unpublished draft.

(76) FAB, personal communication, 1981.

(77) Francis C. Neri, op. cit., p. 1.

(78) "Restricted Pesticides in the Philippines", revised October 1980, FPA, 4 November 1980.

(79) FAB, personal communication, 1981.

(80) Memorandum from Executive Director of the National Food and Agriculture Council, 29 June 1980 — list attached.

(81) *Indian Express*, 9 September 1980.

(82) In interview with the author, 13 September 1980, confirmed in writing, 23 February 1982.

(83) Personal communication in response to questionnaire, 1980.

(84) Ross Unit for Occupational Health, Bangalore, in interview with the author, 17–18 September 1980.

(85) *Guardian*, 9 May 1980.

(86) WHO, *Chemistry and Specifications of Pesticides*, 2nd Report of WHO expert committee on Vector Biology and Control, Technical Report Series 620, Geneva, 1978, p. 7.

(87) USAID, *Environmental Impact Statement on the AID Pest Management Program*, Vol. 1, Washington DC, 1977, pp. 227–8.

(88) W.E. Yates, R.C. Maxwell and J.H. Davis, *Analysis of Pesticide Use in Pakistan*, UC/AID, 1974.

(89) Proposals for the control of pesticide exports are discussed in detail in Chapter 11.

(90) UC/AID, *The Agromedical Approach to Pesticide Management*, January 1976.

Chapter 5: Notes and References

(1) Letter from a development agency worker in Ghana to his local branch of USAID, 2 December 1979.

(2) Ramesh V. Bhat, "Pesticides: A Necessary Evil", *Medico Friends Circle Bulletin*, No. 19, Poona, Jan. 1981, pp. 1–2.

(3) — Ibid., p. 1.

— Statement of Natural Resources Defense Council to the Subcommittee on International Economic Policy and Trade, House Foreign Affairs Committee, Concerning Exports of Hazardous Products, June 5 1980, NRDC, Washington DC, p. 4.

— Anthony Tucker, "Death in the Earth", *Guardian*, 9 March 1972.

— Edward Hughes, "How the Pink Death Came to Iraq", *Sunday Times of India*, 9 September 1973, pp. 17–19.

(4) — *Codex Committee on Pesticide Residues: Explanatory Note*, a Ministry of Agriculture, Fisheries and Food leaflet.

— N. van Tiel, "Activities of the FAO/WHO Codex Alimentarius Commission in the Field of Pesticide Residues", *Outlook on Agriculture*, Vol. 10, No. 3, 1979, pp. 130–134.

(5) Dr. Sudha Nagarkatti, Indian Institute of Horticultural Research, Bangalore, in interview with the author, 19 September 1980.

(6) R.L. Kalra and R.P. Chawla, "Practical Considerations in the Regulation of Pesticide Residues in Food in India", in Edwards, Veeresh and Krueger (eds), *Pesticide Residues in the Environment in India*, Univ. of Agricultural Sciences, Bangalore, 1980, pp. 106–112.

(7) Bhat, op. cit., p. 2.

(8) Kalra and Chawla, in Edwards, Veeresh and Krueger (eds), op. cit., p. 109.

(9) P. Lalitha and V.G. Prasad, "A Review of Work Done in India on Insecticide Residues on/in Vegetables", in Edwards, Veeresh and Krueger (eds), op. cit., pp. 120–145.

(10)   B.S. Attri, S.W. Sarode and Rattanlal, "Insecticide Residues in Vegetables Following Effective Chemical Control Schedules", in Edwards, Veeresh and Krueger (eds), op. cit., pp. 150–165.

(11)   Kalra and Chawla, in Edwards, Veeresh and Krueger (eds), op. cit., pp. 109–110.

(12)   H.C. Agarwal, "Pesticide Residues in Man in India", in Edwards, Veeresh and Krueger (eds), op. cit., pp. 45–56.

(13)   David Kinyanjui, "Pesticide Control: The Kenyan Case", Research Workshop on Perception of Pests and Pesticides in IPM, Clark University, Worcester, Mass., October 1980, p. 9.

(14)   N. Ramasundaram, S. Nagarajah, W.G. Nandasiri and H.R.J.T. Peiris, "A Survey of Organochlorine Insecticide Residues in Sri Lanka", Tropical Agriculturist, 134, No. 2, 1978 (in press).

(15)   Dr. Elikewela, Entomologist, Central Agricultural Research Institute, Sri Lanka, in interview with the author, 8 September 1980.

(16)   Fortnightly meeting of village-level extension workers, Teldeniya Agricultural Productivity Centre, Sri Lanka, attended by the author, 9 September 1980.

(17)   Kalra and Chawla, op. cit., p. 110.

(18)   Proceedings of the US Strategy Conference on Pesticide Management, Washington DC, 7–8 June 1979, Teknekron Research Inc., 1979, p. 46.

(19)   Kalra and Chawla, op. cit., p. 108.

(20)   "Control of Pesticide Residues in Food in the United Kingdom", Ministry of Agriculture, Fisheries and Food, (mimeo).

(21)   K. Butler, Environmental Pollution, Pesticides and Infestation Control Division, Ministry of Agriculture, Fisheries and Food, personal communication, 14 April 1981.

(22)   Esther Peterson and Robert Harris, "Background Report on the Executive Order on Federal Policy Regarding the Export of Banned or Significantly Restricted Substances", The White House, January 1981, p. 10.

(23)   General Accounting Office (GAO) Report to the Congress of the United States – Better Regulation of Pesticide Exports and Pesticide Residues in Imported Food is Essential, Washington DC, 1979, pp. 12–15.

(24)   Sheldon W. Samuels and Richard Cleary, "Comment on Proposed Rules for the Assessment of AID Related Projects", Section Industrial Union Department, AFL-CIO, (mimeo), 1978, p. 3 and appendix.

(25)   Ibid., pp. 3–4.

(26)   W.E. Yates, R.C. Maxwell & J.H. Davis, Analysis of Pesticide Use in Pakistan: A Multidisciplinary Study Team Report, UC/AID, 1974, p. 27.

(27)   ICAITI, An Environmental and Economic Study of the Consequences of Pesticide Use in Central American Cotton Production, Guatemala, 1977.

(28)   Ibid., p. 151.

(29)   Banpot Napompeth, "Impact of Pesticide Laws in Thailand", in Philip S. Motooka (ed), Proceedings of Conference on the Impact of Pesticide Laws, East-West Center, Honolulu, Hawaii, Dec. 6–10, 1976, p. 54.

(30)   Michael Watt, Central Agricultural Research Institute, Gannoruwa, Sri Lanka, in interview with the author, 9 September 1980.

(31)   Dr. Wickremasinghe, Deputy Director, Central Agricultural Research Institute, Sri Lanka, in interview with the author, 8 September 1980.

(32)   Echandi, Kroke, Nigh, Shenk and Weekman, Crop Protection in Brazil, Uruguay, Bolivia, Ecuador and Dominican Republic, UC/AID, 1972, pp. 26 & 34.

Chapter 6 — Notes and References

(1)   —   Ramesh V. Bhat and K.A.V.R. Krishnamachari, "Endemic Familial Arthritis of Malnad — An epidemiological study", Indian J. Med. Res., 66, 5 Nov. 1977, pp. 777–786.

       —   Krishnamachari and Bhat, "Endemic Familial Arthritis of Malnad. An Outbreak in Southern India", Tropical and Geographical Medicine, 30 (1978), pp. 33–37.

       —   Bhat and Krishnamachari, "Food Toxins and Disease Outbreaks in India," Arogya — J. Health Sci., 1978, IV, pp. 92–100.

- Bhat, "Pesticides: A Necessary Evil", *Medico Friends Circle Bulletin*, 19 January 1981.
- "Indian bone disease blamed on pesticides", *New Scientist*, 18 September 1977, p. 395.
- Dr. Ravi Narayan, St. John's Medical College, Bangalore, Karnataka, in an interview with the author, 18 September 1980.

(2) David Pimentel et al., "A Cost-Benefit Analysis of Pesticide Use in US Food Production" in Pimentel and Sheets (eds), *Pesticides: Their Contemporary Roles in Agriculture, Health and the Environment*, Humana Press, 1979, p. 130.

(3) UC/AID, *International Survey on Pesticide Use*, 1972, p. 9.

(4) Ingrid Palmer, *Science and Agricultural Production*, UNRISD, Geneva, 1972, p. 77.

(5) USAID, *Environmental Impact Statement (EIS) on the AID Pest Management Program*, 1977, Vol. 2, p. 353.

(6) Ibid.

(7) USAID, op. cit., Vol. 1, p. 235.

(8) Palmer, op. cit.

(9) K.I. Sudderuddin and R.P. Kim, "The Effect of Pesticides on Paddy-Field Ecosystems", *Proc. Confr. Trends in Applied Biology*, USM, Penang, Oct. 1979.

(10) Ibid.

(11) Dr. Ishmael Sudderuddin, Dept. of Zoology, University of Malaya, in interview with the author, 23 September 1980.

(12) G.S. Lim and S.H. Ong, *Pesticide Benefits and Side Effects*, Southeast Asian Workshop in Pesticide Management, Bangkok, 1977.

(13) Punla Foundation Inc., Quezon City, Philippines, *Rural Poverty Series*, January 1981.

(14)
- UC/AID , *Plant Protection in Bangladesh: A multi-disciplinary study team report*, 1975.
- Dr. Fred Simmonds, ex Director, Commonwealth Institute for Biological Control, in interview with the author, 18 September 1980.

(15) ICAITI, *An Environmental and Economic Study of the Consequences of Pesticide Use in Central American Cotton Production*, Final Report, Second Edition, Guatemala, 1977.

(16) W. R. Thompson, letter to *The Salisbury Herald*.

(17) But see manufacturer's comment in Chapter 4, p.40

(18) SCONE Bulletin, Quarter Ending September 1981, Issue No. 3, Editorial. Oxfam Project, BD 114.

(19) Lim and Ong, op. cit.

(20) Ibid.

(21) David Pimentel, et al., "Environmental and social costs of pesticides: a preliminary assessment", *OIKOS* 34: 124–140, Copenhagen, 1980.

(22) In Francine Schulberg, "United States Export of Products Banned for Domestic Use", *Harvard International Law Journal*, Vol. 20, No. 2, Spring 1979, pp. 364–5.

(23) UC/AID (1972), op. cit., p. 9.

Chapter 7 — Notes and References

(1) *The Guardian*, 22 July 1980. This letter was largely about the use of 2, 4, 5–T in Britain. The fact that this argument about the Third World was included serves to demonstrate the importance of this issue to the industry.

(2) *Pesticides in the Modern World*. A symposium prepared by members of the Co-operative Programme of Agro-Allied Industries with FAO and other United Nations Organisations, 1972, p. 21.

(3)
- David Pimentel et al., "Benefits and Costs of Pesticide Use in US Food Production", *BioScience*, Vol. 28, No. 12, 1978.
- David Pimental et al., "Benefits and Costs of Pesticide Use in US Food Production", in T.J. Sheets and D. Pimentel (eds), *Pesticides: Their Contemporary Roles in Agriculture, Health and the Environment*, the Humana Press, Clifton,

New Jersey, 1979, pp. 97–149.

- David Pimentel et al., "Environmental and Social Costs of Pesticides: a Preliminary Assessment", *OIKOS* 34: 126–140, Copenhagen, 1980.

(4) Pimentel, 1978, op. cit., p. 782.

(5) – *Restoring the Quality of Environment*, Rept. Environmental Pollution Panel, Pres. Sci. Adv. Comm., The White House, Washington DC, 1965.

- J.C. Headley, "Productivity of Agricultural Pesticides" in "Economic Research on Pesticides for Policy Decision Making" *Proc. Symp. Econ. Res. Serv.*, US Dept. of Agriculture, 1971, pp. 80–88.

- D. Pimentel, "Extent of Pesticide Use, Food Supply, and Pollution", *J.N.Y. Entomol. Soc.* 81, 1973, pp. 13–33.

(6) Pimentel, 1980, op. cit., p. 135.

(7) See, for example, OECD, *Report of the Steering Group on Pest Control Under the Conditions of Small Farmer Food Crop Production in Developing Countries*, Paris, 1979, p. 15.

Other sources, though, disagree. See, for example, USAID, *Environmental Impact Statement on the AID Pest Management Program*, Dept. of State, Washington DC, 1977, Vol. 1, p. 324.

(8) Gordon R. Conway (ed), "Pesticide Resistance and World Food Production", Imperial College of Science and Technology, London, 1980, (mimeo) para. 17.

(9) Grace Goodell, *Consequences of the New HYV Technology*, unpublished draft.

(10) Barbara A. Barr, Carlton S. Koehler and Ray F. Smith, *Crop Losses: Rice: Field Losses to Insects, Diseases, Weeds and Other Pests*, UC/AID, 1975, p. 21.

(11) In interview with the author, September 1980.

(12) The full AID study, which led to the adoption of this policy and describes it in full, is contained in the two volumes of "Environmental Impact Statement on the AID Pest Management Program", dated 13 May 1977, and produced by the United States Agency for International Development, Department of State, Washington DC.

(13) USAID, op. cit., Vol. I, p. 29.

(14) Ibid., pp. 50–51.

(15) Environmental Defense Fund, National Audubon Society, Natural Resources Defense Council, and the Sierra Club.

(16) The five alternatives considered were:

A. To continue AID pest management activities as they were prior to December 1975.

B. That any proposed pesticide activity be evaluated, taking into consideration the US regulatory status of the pesticide and, if approved, that technical assistance be provided to ensure safe and effective use.

C. To continue according to the interim regulations adopted after the legal case. These said that, except in specified circumstances, AID would not supply DDT, aldrin, dieldrin, 2, 4, 5–T, chlordane, heptachlor or any banned, suspended or unregistered pesticide. The exceptions allowed, for example, the continued use of DDT for vector control. (These regulations are explained more fully on pages 108–109 of the EIS.)

D. Elimination of all pesticides from AID programmes, other pest management activity unchanged.

E. Elimination of all pest management assistance.

(17) USAID, op. cit., p. xix.

(18) Ibid., p. xx.

(19) Personal communication, 3 September 1981.

(20) R.O. Blake et al., *Aiding the Environment: A Study of the Environmental Policies, Procedures and Performance of the US Agency for International Development*, Natural Resources Defense Council, Washington DC, 1980, p. 173.

(21) Dr. Virgil M. Freed, Head of Dept. of Agricultural Chemistry and Director of Environmental Health Sciences Center, Oregon State University, in *Proceedings of the US Strategy Conference on Pesticide Management*, sponsored by Dept. of State and US National Committee for Man and the Biosphere, Washington DC, June 1979, published by Teknekron Research Inc., p. 25.

(22) ICAITI, *An Environmental and Economic Study of the Consequences of Pesticide Use in Central American Cotton Production*, Final Report, 2nd Edition, Guatemala, 1977, pp. 155-164.

(23) Roy D. Wilcoxson, M.T. Ali Niazee, E. Dresner, Glenn W. Hedlund and Richard C. Maxwell, *Plant Protection in Bangladesh: a multi-disciplinary study team report*, UC/AID, 1975, pp. 35-40.

(24) Ibid., p. 40.

Chapter 8 — Notes and References

(1) ICAITI. *An Environmental and Economic Study of the Consequences of Pesticide Use in Central American Cotton Production*, Final Report, Second Edition, Guatemala, 1977, p. 125.

(2) Ibid., p. 124.

(3) Ibid., p. 242.

(4) Dr. J. Jeyeratnam, Dept. of Community Medicine, Faculty of Medicine, Colombo, Sri Lanka. In interview with the author, 1 September 1980.

(5) ICAITI, op. cit., p. 199.

(6) Dr. Ravi Narayan, Ross Unit for Occupational Health, St. John's Medical College, Bangalore, India. In interview with the author, 20 September 1980.

(7) Andrew Pearse, *Seeds of Plenty, Seeds of Want: Social and Economic Implications of the Green Revolution*, Clarendon Press, Oxford, 1980, p. 51.

(8) William R. Furtick and Ray F. Smith, "World Problems of Pesticides" in *The Agro-medical Approach to Pesticide Management*, UC/AID, 1976, p. 10.

(9) ICAITI, op. cit., pp. 26-27.

(10) Georganne Chapin and Robert Wasserstrom, "Agricultural Production and Malaria Resurgence in Central America and India", *Nature*, Vol. 293, 17 September 1981, p. 182.

(11) David Weir and Mark Schapiro, *Circle of Poison*, Institute for Food and Development Policy, San Francisco, 1981, p. 33.

(12) Weir and Schapiro, Ibid., p. 36.

(13) David Pimentel et al., "Pesticides, Insects in Foods, and Cosmetic Standards". *Bio Science*, Vol. 27, No. 3, March 1977, p. 183. Pimentel estimates that 10-20% *additional* insecticide is used for these purposes. This would equal about 9-16% of total insecticide use on those crops.

(14) G.A. Norton and G.R. Conway, "The Economic and Social Context of Pest, Disease and Weed Problems", in J.M. Cherrett and G.R. Sagar (eds) *Origins of Pest, Parasite, Disease and Weed Problems*, Blackwell Scientific Publications, Oxford, 1977, pp. 212-214.

(15) — Bharat Dogra, personal communication, 1980.

— OECD, *Report of the Steering Group on Pest Control Under the Conditions of Small Farmer Food Crop Production in Developing Countries*, Paris, 1977, p. 25.

(16) Andrew Clark, OXFAM, Madhya Pradesh, India, personal communication, February 1981.

(17) — *Pest Control: An Assessment of Present and Alternative Technologies: Vol. V: Pest Control and Public Health*, National Academy of Sciences, Washington DC, 1976, p. 251.

— Ingrid Palmer, *Science and Agricultural Production*, UNRISD, Geneva, 1972, pp. 64-5.

— David Pimentel, *Socioeconomic Costs & Benefits of Pesticide Use*, South-east Asian Workshop on Pesticide management, Bangkok, 1977, p. 2.

(18) Norton and Conway, op. cit., p. 212.

(19) Pearse, op. cit., p. 100.

(20) Ibid., p. 166.

(21) Ibid., p. 172.

(22) National Academy of Sciences, op. cit. (see ref. 17), pp. 262-3.

(23) USAID, *Environmental Impact Statement on the AID Pest Management Program*, USAID, Dept. of State, Washington DC, 1977, Vol. 1, p. 275.

(24) Pearse, op. cit., p. 207.

(25) A more comprehensive discussion of land tenure and the very poor appears in Claire Whittemore, *Land for People*, Oxfam Public Affairs Unit, Oxford, 1981.

Chapter 9 —Notes and References

(1) Mr. Frederick J. Rarig, Vice-President Rohm & Haas Co., quoted from *Proceedings of the US Strategy Conference on Pesticide Management*, June 1979, Washington DC, p. 25.

(2) ICAITI, *An Environmental and Economic Study of the Consequences of Pesticide Use in Central American Cotton Production* Final Report, Second Edition, Guatemala, 1977, p. 193.

(3) Rarig, op. cit., p. 31.

(4) David Weir and Mark Schapiro, *Circle of Poison*, Institute for Food and Development Policy, San Francisco, 1981, p. 16.

(5) K. Moody et al., Philippine Journal of Weed Science (7:57–69), reported in *Tropical Pest Management*, Vol. 27, No. 3, September 1981, pp. 428-9.

(6) ILO, *Safety and Health in Agricultural Work*, Geneva, 1965 (2nd impression 1973), pp. 91-2.

(7) ILO, *Safe Use of Pesticides*, Occupational Safety and Health Series, No. 38, Geneva, 1977 (2nd impression 1979), p. 4.

(8) FAO, *Ad Hoc Government Consultation on International Standardisation of Pesticide Registration Requirements*, 24–28 October 1977, Rome, 1977, pp. 26 and 32.

(9) Banpot Napompeth, "Thailand: National Profile on Pest Management and Related Problems", 1980, (mimeo) p. 24.

(10) Schweizer and Banthien, Hoechst Aktengesellschaft in letter to Hoechst UK Ltd (1 March 1982) in response to OXFAM's enquiries.

(11) Joyce Tait, personal communication, 10 September 1981.

(12) Mr. B.N. Fox & Dr. R. Tincknell, Shell International Chem. Co., London, in interview with the author, 17 November 1981, and subsequent letter from B.N. Fox, 23 April 1982.

(13) T.W. Parton and H. Aebi, Ciba-Geigy Ltd, personal communication, 15 December 1981.

(14) T.W. Parton and H. Aebi, personal communication, 23 February 1982.

(15) Letter from Deanna Donovan to Institute of Current World Affairs, USA, 18 October 1979.

(16) World Bank, 1980 World Development Report, Washington DC, 1980.

(17) Mr. Percy Abeywardena in interview with the author, 8 September 1980.

(18) In interview with the author, 20 September 1980.

(19) Discussion at a meeting of extension workers at Teldeniya Agricultural Productivity Centre, Sri Lanka, 9 September 1980.

(20) ICI argue that the message is directed at professional advisors or plantation managers who would not receive any false impression. They are satisfied that "the advertisement is fair and reasonable". B.W. Cox, Manager, Publicity Department, ICI Plant Protection Division, personal communication, 14 December 1981.

(21) CCTA, "National Enquiry into Popular Technology in the Control of Pests and Diseases", a letter from Hans Carlier of CCTA. OXFAM project file, Peru 121.

(22) *Minka*, No. 6., June 1981, p. 3. OXFAM project file, Peru 121.

(23) Grace Goodell, *Consequences of the New HYV Technology*, unpublished draft, p. 11.

(24) International Chamber of Commerce (ICC), *International Codes of Marketing Practice*, Paris, 1974.

(25) Ibid. p. 43.

(26) Ibid.

(27) Ibid., p. 44.

(28) Ibid., p. 47.

(29) Ibid., p. 49.

(30) Ibid., p. 54.

(31) Dr. A. Balasubramaniam, Secretary, Pesticides Board, Malaysia, personal communication, 14 July 1981.

(32) These rules are issued under the Pesticides Act, 1974.

(33) Mr. Chris Major, Director of BAA, in interview with the author, 17 July 1981, subsequently confirmed in writing.

(34) Directive 79/117/EEC, *Official Journal of European Communities*, L33, Vol. 22, 8 February 1979. The directive is in force from 1 January 1981.

(35) "Suspended and Cancelled Pesticides", US Environmental Protection Agency, Washington DC, 2nd revision, October 1979.

(36) Dr. A. Balasubramaniam, personal communication, 14 July 1981.

(37) WHO/F AO, Data Sheets on Pesticides, Chlordane, VBC/DS/78.36, issued June 1978.

(38) Richard F. Blewitt, Vice-President, Corporate Affairs, Velsicol Chemical Corporation, personal communication, 14 December 1981.

(39) Ibid.

(40) National Union of Agricultural and Allied Workers (NUAAW), *Not One Minute Longer*, London 1980, p. 12.

(41) WHO/FAO, Data Sheets on Pesticides, 2, 4, 5-T, VBC/DS/75.13, 1975.

(42) B.W. Cox, ICI, personal communication, 14 December 1981.

(43) V. Freed, "Storage, Handling and Disposal of Chemicals" in *The Agromedical Approach to Pesticide Management*, UC/AID, 1976, p. 107.

(44) Dr. Graham Matthews, Overseas Spraying Machinery Centre, Silwood Park, Ascot, in interview with the author, 29 January 1981.

(45) WHO/FAO, Data Sheets on Pesticides, Lindane, VBC/DS/75.12, 1975.

(46) B.W. Cox, ICI, personal communication, 14 December 1981.

(47) Gary Jones, Manager, Communications, Pacific Area, Dow Chemical Pacific Ltd, personal communication, 11 December 1981.

(48) WHO/FAO, Data Sheets on Pesticides, Chlorpyrifos, VBC/DS/75.18, 1975.

(49) Peter Varey, Central Public Relations Manager, FBC Ltd, personal communication, 16 September 1981.

(50) Article 42, "Reglamento Relativo a la Importacion, Elaboracion, Almacenamiento, Transporte, Venta y Uso de Pesticidas", 1974.

(51) Werner Gebauer, Bayer AG, personal communication, 11 February 1982.

(52) *South*, November 1980, p. 8.

(53) C. Satake, Deputy Manager, International Business Dept., Sumitomo Chemical Co. Ltd, Pesticides Division, personal communication, 8 September 1981.

(54) C. Satake, Sumitomo Chemical Company Ltd, personal communication, 6 November 1981.

(55) WHO/FAO, Data Sheet on Pesticides, Dimethoate, VBC/DS/80.42, 1980, p. 5.

(56) Dott. Michele Faldella, Farmoplant (Montedison), Milan, 31 March 1982.

(57) Peter Varey, Central Public Relations Manager, FBC Ltd, personal communication, 16 September 1981.

(58) John E. Lafferty, Manager, International Communications, FMC Corporation, personal communication, 4 December 1981.

(59) OECD, *Report of the Steering Group on Pest Control Under the Conditions of Small Farmer Food Crop Production in Developing Countries*, Paris, pp. 26–7.

(60) B.N. Fox and Dr. Tincknell, Shell International Chemical Company Ltd, in interview with the author, 17 November 1981.

(61) Meeting between the author, B.W. Cox, ICI Publicity Manager, and others, 29 September 1981.

(62) K.L. Heong, MARDI, personal communication, 21 October 1981. While pointing out that insecticides in granular form are less injurious to natural enemies, Dr. Heong goes on to say that,

"From 1977 onwards, we only recommend the use of insecticides against stemborers in what we describe as 'endemic' areas. This was determined by records obtained in the previous season. Should the % white heads (symptom of borer attack) taken towards the end of the crop exceed a threshold (5% was used), granules were recommended to be used prophylactically in the following season.

"In view of the present low status of stemborers, our latest recommendation is to avoid using insecticides if possible. Should it be necessary, then granules should be used, BHC being one of them. Farmers are advised to examine their fields every 10 days until the maximum tillering stage. If dead hearts . . . in the nurseries exceed 3% or 10% in the planted crop, the insecticides should be applied.

"You will see that we have gone away from the calendar spray recommendation of the past to the use of thresholds. At the beginning we used a threshold of the previous season's attack. This is because when symptoms are observed it will be too late. Later we realised that although the plant may suffer some 'dead hearts' it can compensate and no yield loss may result . . . Thus the later recommendations."

(63) B.W. Cox, ICI, personal communication, 14 December 1981.
(64) In interview with the author, 8 September 1980.
(65) *Proceedings of the US Strategy Conference on Pesticide Management*, Washington DC, 1979, pp. 61–2.

Chapter 10 — Notes and References

(1)   Paul DeBach, *Biological Control by Natural Enemies*, Cambridge University Press, 1974, p. 271.
(2)   OECD, *Report of the Steering Group on Pest Control Under the Conditions of Small Farmer Food Crop Production in Developing Countries*, OECD Planning Group on Science and Technology for Developing Countries, Paris, 1977, pp. 25–7.
(3)   Ray F. Smith and J. Lawrence Apple, "Principles of Integrated Pest Control" in *Short Course on Integrated Pest Control for Irrigated Rice in South and South East Asia*, Philippines, 1978.
(4)   OECD, op. cit., p. 30.
(5)   Commonweatlh Agricultural Bureaux, *Biological Control Service*, HMSO, London, 1976, p. 11.
(6)   —   Ibid.
      —   Dr. Fred Simmonds, ex Director, Commonwealth Institute for Biological Control, in interview with the author, 18 September 1980.
(7)   DeBach, op. cit., pp. 191–4.
(8)   OECD, op. cit., p. 30.
(9)   J.E. Davies, Virgil H. Freed and Ray F. Smith, "Agromedical Approaches to Pesticide Management" in *The Agromedical Approach to Pesticide Management*, UC/AID, 1976, pp. 1–2.
(10) *Pesticides in the Modern World*, a Symposium prepared by members of the Co-operative Programme of Agro-Allied Industries with FAO and other United Nations Organisations, 1972, p. 54.
(11) Personal communication, 1980.
(12) OECD, op. cit., p. 27.
(13) G.R. Conway, "Ecological Aspects of Pest Control in Malaysia", in M.T. Farvar and J.P. Milton (eds), *The Careless Technology*, Natural History Press, New York, 1971.
(14) DeBach, op. cit., p. 294.
(15) ICAITI, *An Environmental and Economic Study of the Consequences of Pesticide Use in Central American Cotton Production*, Final Report, Second Edition, Guatemala, 1977, p. 133.
(16) Ibid., p. 141.
(17) Ibid., p. 144.
(18) FAO/UNEP, *The Development and Application of Integrated Pest Control in Agriculture: Formulation of a Co-operative Global Programme*, Report on an ad hoc

session of the FAO Panel of Experts on Integrated Pest Control held in Rome, 15-25 October 1974, FAO, Rome, 1975, Appendix B, p. 1.

(19) Ibid., Appendix B, p. 2.

(20) ICAITI, op. cit., p. 260.

(21) FAO/UNEP, op. cit.

(22) ICAITI, op. cit., Table 27, p. 97.

(23) FAO/UNEP, op. cit.

(24) Ibid., Appendix B, pp. 14–15.

(25) ICAITI, op. cit., p. 260.

(26) M.J. Way, "Integrated Control — practical realities", *Outlook on Agriculture*, Vol. 9, No. 3, 1977, p. 127.

(27) Mr Lin Yu, Deputy President of the Institute for Plant Protection, Jiangsu Academy of Agricultural Sciences, Shaolingwei, Nanjing, in interview with Adrian Moyes of OXFAM's Public Affairs Unit, 13 September 1980.

(28) Boel Berner, *The Organisation and Economy of Pest Control in China*, Research Policy Institute, University of Lund, Sweden, Discussion Paper, No. 128, July 1979, p. 42.

(29) Ibid., pp. 42–3.

(30) Ibid., p. 53.

(31) Ibid., pp. 53–4.

(32) The discussion of the Orissa programme is based on the following sources:
  — OECD, op. cit., Annex II, pp. 63–68.
  — J.P. Kulshreshtha, "Integrated pest management programme in operation in India", (mimeo) International Rice Research Conference, IRRI, 1976.
  — J.P. Kulshrestha, "Integrated Management of Rice Insect Pests", (mimeo).
  — Annual Reports of Operational Research Project on Integrated Control of Rice Pests in Orissa for the years 1976 & 1979.

(33) 1976 Annual Report, ibid.

(34) OECD, op. cit., p. 65.

(35) 1979 Annual Report, op. cit.

(36) Bill Reed, Principal Entomologist, Pulses, ICRISAT, personal communication, 29 June 1981.

(37) Lucas Brader, personal communication, 10 February 1981.

(38) FAO/UNEP, *Integrated Pest Control*, Report of the Ninth Session of the FAO/UNEP Panel of Experts held in the Sudan, 9–13 December 1979, Rome, 1980, p. 6.

(39) Ibid., p. 27.

(40) DeBach, op. cit., p. 280.

(41) Ray F. Smith, "The Strategy of Integrated Pest Control and Pest Management", in *Procs. of the UC/AID — University of Alexandria, Seminar/Workshop in Pesticide Management*, 5–10 March, 1977, UC/AID, 1977, p. 13.

(42) Ibid., p. 15.

(43) Way, op. cit., pp. 127–8.

(44) *Worcester Telegram*, 1 October 1980.

(45) Melot Balisalisa, Pesticides Study Co-ordinator, Farmers Assistance Board, personal communication, 27 March 1981.

(46) Reed, op. cit.

(47) FAO, *Model Extension Leaflet on Pest Resistance to Pesticides*, prepared for FAO by Andrew S. Deal, Extension Entomologist, University of California, Riverside, Rome, 1971, p. 6.

(48) Way, op. cit., p. 134.

(49) OECD, op. cit., pp. 33–4.

(50) P.T. Haskell, "Integrated pest control and small farmer crop protection in developing countries", *Outlook on Agriculture*, 9 March 1977, p. 124.

(51) Ibid.

(52) Ibid., p. 126.

(53) Chris Major, Director, BAA, in interview with the author, 17 July 1981, confirmed in writing.

Chapter 11 — Notes and References

(1) A.V. Adam, "The Importance of Pesticides in Developing Countries" in D.L. Gunn and J.G.R. Stevens, *Pesticides and Human Welfare*, Oxford University Press, 1976, p. 126.

(2) — The Gazette of the Democratic Socialist Republic of Sri Lanka, Part II of 16 May 1980; Supplement (issued 23 May 1980) Control of Pesticides: A Bill.

     — The Gazette of the Democratic Socialist Republic of Sri Lanka, Supplement to Part II of 3 October 1980, Control of Pesticides Act No. 33 of 1980, Certified on 5 September 1980.

(3) See Chapter 4 for further details.

(4) — A. Balasubramaniam, *Pesticides Act, 1974*, Seminar on Health Food and Nutrition, Consumers Association of Penang, 15–20 September 1979.

     — A. Balasubramaniam, *Status of Pesticides Usage and Their Control in Peninsular Malaysia*, Southeast Asian Workshop on Pesticide Management, Bangkok, 1977.

     — A. Balasubramaniam, Senior Agricultural Officer (Pesticides), Dept. of Agriculture, Ministry of Agriculture, Kuala Lumpur, Malaysia, in interview with the author, 23 September 1980.

     — The [Malaysia] Pesticides Act, 1974.

(5) See Chapter 9 for details.

(6) Kathy Adams, *A Preliminary Investigation of Some Aspects of the Use of Insecticides and Pesticides in Zimbabwe*; a report to the Public Affairs Unit, OXFAM, Oxford; Salisbury, February 1981. Relevant regulations include Hazardous Substance and Articles Regulations of 1979 and 1980.

(7) *The Hindu*, 26 July 1981.

(8) David Kinyanjui, *Pesticide Control: The Kenyan Case*, Background Paper No. 4, Research Workshop on the Perception of Pests and Pesticides in Integrated Pest Management, Clark University, Worcester, Mass., 5–8 October 1980, p. 11.

(9) Ibid., p. 21.

(10) Ibid., p. 24.

(11) — Banpot Napompeth, "Thailand, National Profile on Pest Management and Related Problems", (mimeo) 1980.

     — Banpot Napompeth, "Impact of Pesticide Laws in Thailand" in Philip S. Motooka (ed), *Procs. Conference on the Impact of Pesticide Laws*, 6–10 December 1976, East-West Centre, Hawaii, pp. 52–55.

(12) Napompeth, 1980, op. cit., pp. 33–4.

(13) "Export of Hazardous Products: Hearings before the Subcommittee on International Economic Policy and Trade of the Committee on Foreign Affairs", House of Representatives 96th Congress, 2nd Session, 5 & 12 June and 9 September 1980, p. 23.

(14) S. Jacob Scherr, in *Procs. of US Strategy Conf. on Pesticide Management*, June 7–8 1979, Washington DC, p. 32.

(15) Frederick J. Rarig, in ibid., p. 29.

(16) UN Economic and Social Council, *Exchange of information on banned hazardous chemicals and unsafe pharmaceutical products*, Report of the Secretary General, 2nd Regular Session, 1–24 July 1981.

(17) Samuel Gitonga, in *Procs. of US Strategy Conf.*, op. cit., p. 41.

(18) Frank A. Del Prado, in *Procs. of US Strategy Conf.*, op. cit., pp. 45–47.

(19) *The Standard*, Nairobi, Kenya, 11 May 1977 and 25 April 1979. This statement has been widely quoted including by Jacob Scherr, US Strategy Conference, op. cit., p. 32; Weir and Schapiro, *Circle of Poison*, p. 66, and *Export of Hazardous Products Hearings*, op. cit., p. 15.

(20) Francine Schulberg, "United States Export of Products Banned for Domestic Use", *Harvard International Law Review*, Vol. 20, No. 2, Spring 1979, p. 366.

(21) Export of Hazardous Products Hearings, op. cit., Appendix 18, p. 405.
(22) Quoted in Schulberg, op. cit., pp. 366–7.
(23) *Consumer Currents*, No. 34, Penang, Feb. 1981, p. 16.
(24) IRPTC Bulletin, Vol. 3, No. 1, Geneva, January 1980, p. 2.
(25) IRPTC Bulletin, Vol. 4, No. 1, Geneva, January 1981, pp. 3–4.
(26) Quoted in Schulberg, op. cit., p. 364.
(27) Ibid., p. 365.
(28) UNEP/GC/Resolution 6/4, 1978, quoted in "Exchange of Information on Banned Hazardous Chemicals and Unsafe Pharmaceutical Products", Report of the Secretary General, UN Economic and Social Council, Second Regular Session, 1–24 July 1981, Annex IV, p. 2.
(29) IRPTC Bulletin, Vol. 2, No. 2, July 1979, p. 4.
(30) UN General Assembly 34th Session, Agenda Item 12, 106th Plenary Meeting 17.12.79 A/RES/34/173, 18 January 1980.
(31) S. Jacob Scherr, "Statement on Behalf of the Natural Resources Defense Council before the House Committee on Agriculture Subcommittee on Department Operations, Research, and Foreign Agriculture, concerning Exports of Banned Pesticides", 22 July 1981, p. 9.
(32) — Ibid., passim.
     — S. Jacob Scherr, personal communication, 10 September 1981.
     — Dr. Jack D. Early, President, National Agricultural Chemicals Association, Statement before the Subcommittee on Department Operations, Research and Foreign Agriculture of the Committee on Agriculture, US House of Representatives, 16 July 1981.
(33) Scherr, July 1981, op. cit., (ref. 31).
(34) Export of Hazardous Products Hearings, op. cit., Appendix 1, pp. 215–9.
(35) Esther Peterson and Robert Harris, "Background Report on the Executive Order on Federal Policy Regarding the Export of Banned or Significantly Restricted Substances", The White House, Washington DC, January 1981, p. 18.
(36) *Los Angeles Times*, 16 January 1981.
(37) Export of Hazardous Products Hearings, op. cit., Appendix 24, p. 414.
(38) Peterson and Harris, op. cit., p. 39.
(39) Early, op. cit.
(40) Richard F. Blewitt, Velsicol Chemical Corporation, personal communication, 14 December 1981.
(41) S. Jacob Scherr, Natural Resources Defense Council, Washington DC, personal communication, 26 February 1981.
(42) Scherr, personal communication, op. cit.
(43) T.W. Parton and H. Aebi, Ciba–Geigy Ltd., personal communication, 23 February 1982.
(44) *International Agricultural Development*, Nov./Dec. 1980, p. 4.
(45) N.J. King, Department of the Environment, personal communication, 22 January 1980.
(46) *Official Journal of the European Communities*, L259, Vol. 22, 15 October 1979, pp. 10–28.
(47) *Official Journal of the European Communities*, L33, Vol. 22, 8 February 1979, pp. 36–40.
(48) Graham Collins, Pesticide Branch, Ministry of Agriculture, Fisheries and Food, personal communication, 9 February 1982.
(49) Ibid.
(50) Agricultural Chemicals Approval Scheme, *Approved Products for Farmers and Growers, 1981*, HMSO, 1981, p. 4.
(51) BASIS, "The Aims, Organisation and Work of BASIS", (leaflet).
(52) The following proposal is based on the Model Export Program devised by Schulberg and Scherr, in Schulberg, op. cit., pp. 378–383.

Here, our proposal is restricted to pesticides, the subject of this book, but could be extended to include other hazardous substances.

(53)   Mary Elizabeth Hoinkes, Deputy Assistant Secretary of State for Oceans and International Environmental and Scientific Affairs, Testimony before the Subcommittee on Operations, Research and Foreign Agriculture, Committee on Agriculture, House of Representatives, 22 July 1981.

(54)   Scherr, July 1981, op. cit., pp. 6–7.

(55)   US Delegation Statement for the Ministerial Level Meeting of the Environment Committee of the OECD, Paris, 7–8 May 1979.

(56)   S. Jacob Scherr, Memorandum re: "Report on the Seminar on Controls of Chemicals in Importing Countries and the First Meeting of the OECD Expert Group on Information Exchange Related to Export of Hazardous Chemicals, April 1981", Natural Resources Defense Council, Washington DC, 12 May 1981.

APPENDICES

Appendix I

INFORMATION ON SELECTED PESTICIDES

Pesticide	LD$_{50}$[1] Oral	LD$_{50}$[1] Dermal	WHO Classification	UK Regulations[3]	EEC Banned or severely restricted [4]	US Banned or severely restricted [5]	Exported from UK to 3rd World [6]
aldicarb	0.93		IA	HSII/P		R	
aldrin	38-54	98	IB		*	SC	
azinphos-ethyl	12		IB	HSIII/P/W			
azinphos-methyl	16		IB	HSIII/P			
BHC (HCH) (other than lindane)	100		II	NL	*	SC	
carbaryl	500	4,000(rabbit)	II				
carbofuran	8		IB	HSII/P		R	
chlordane	335	690	II		*	SC	
chlorfenvinphos	10		IA	HSIII/P			
chlorpyrifos	135	202	II				*
DBCP	170		IA	NL		SC	
DDT	250	250-500 (in oil) 2,510 (as powder)	II		*	SC	
demeton-S-methyl	40		IB	HSIII/P			*
demeton-S-methyl sulphone	37		IB	HSIII/P			*
diazinon	300	2,150	II				
dichlorvos	56	75	IB	HSIII/P			
dicrotophos	22		IB	NL		R	
dieldrin	46	60[7]	IA	W	*	SC	
dimethoate	cl50	353	II				
dinoseb	58		IB	HSII/P			*
disulfoton	2.6		IA	HSII/P		R	*
DNOC	25		IB	HSII/P			*
endosulfan	40-50	130-681	II	HSII/P			
endrin	7.5	15	IB	HSII/P	*	SC	
fenitrothion	503	1,300[8]	II				
heptachlor	100	195	II	W	*	SC	*10
leptophos	43	800 (rabbit)	IA	NL		unregistered	
lindane (99% gamma HCH)	88-225	900	II			SC	
malathion	1,000	4,444	III				
methamidophos	30		IB	NL		R	
methomyl	17		IB	HSII/P			
mevinphos	3.7	4.2	IA	HSII/P			
monocrotophos	14	112[9]	IB	NL			
omethoate	50		IB	HSIII/P			
oxydemeton-methyl	65	250	IB	HSIII/P			
paraquat	100	80	II	P			
parathion-ethyl	3.6	6.8	IA	HSII/P		SC	
parathion-methyl	14	67	IA	NL			
pentachlorophenol	27		IB				
phenylmercury acetate	30		IA	P	*	SC	*
phorate	2		IA	HSII/P		R	*
phosphamidon	17	107-143	IA	HSII/P			*
pirimiphos-ethyl	140		IB	HSIII/P			
propoxur	95	2,400	II				
2, 4, 5-T	500		II			SC	*

(1) The figures given are LD$_{50}$ rat unless stated otherwise and are measured in mg/kg.

Sources: WHO/FAO Data Sheets on Pesticides. Where a choice of figures (eg male or female rat) are available, the lowest figure is given.

Guidelines to the Use of the WHO Recommended Classification of Pesticides by Hazard, VBC/78. 1 Rev.1, Revision May 1979, WHO.

USAID, Environmental Impact Statement, 1977, Vol II, Appendix B.

Where these sources differ, priority is given in the order listed above.

(2) Source: Guidelines to the Use of the WHO Recommended Classification of Pesticides by Hazard.

Class IA — "extremely hazardous"
Class IB — "highly hazardous"
Class II — "moderately hazardous"
Class III — "slightly hazardous"

In addition to these four classes, there is a fifth list: "list of technical products unlikely to present acute hazard in normal use".

(3)   'HSII' or 'HSIII' indicate that the substance is specified in Part two or Part three of the Health and Safety (Agriculture) (Poisonous Substances) Regulations, 1975. These regulations impose obligations on employers and workers regarding age limits, training and supervision, hours of work etc and specify protective clothing which must be worn. A register of operations using these substances must be kept and certain safety precautions followed. A summary of these regulations appears in the booklet, "Poisonous Chemicals on the Farm", Health and Safety series booklet HS(G)2, HMSO, London, 1980.

'P' indicates that the substance is included in the Poisons List (Poisons List Order 1978) and is subject to the Poisons Rules (1978) made under The Poisons Act, 1972. These rules restrict the sale of listed poisons and make specific rules for their labelling. All poisons included in this Appendix (except paraquat) must, for example, be labelled with the words "Caution. This substance is poisonous. The inhalation of its vapour, mist, spray or dust may have harmful consequences. It may also be dangerous to let it come into contact with the skin or clothing." Some of the substances are exempted from the Poisons Rules if prepared in specified ways (eg granular preparations).

'NL' indicates that the substance is not listed in the recommendations sheets "Chemical Compounds Used as Pesticides: Recommendations for Safe Use in the United Kingdom".

'W' indicates that the recommendations sheet for the use of this substance in agriculture and horticulture has been withdrawn.

(4)   *Source:*   EEC Council Directive 79/117/EEC of 21 December 1978 prohibiting the placing on the market and use of plant protection products containing certain active substances, Annex. *Official Journal of the European Communities,* L33, Volume 22, 8 February 1979, pp.39-40.
An asterisk indicates that the pesticide concerned is covered by the above directive.

(5)   'SC' indicates that the substance is included in the list of "Suspended and Cancelled Pesticides" (2nd revision, October 1979, OPA 159/9) issued by the US Environmental Protection Agency. Some or all uses of these products have been suspended, cancelled or otherwise restricted in the USA.

'R' indicates that the active ingredient concerned is listed under the following heading: "the following uses of pesticide products containing the active ingredients specified below have been classified for restricted use and are limited to use by or under the direct supervision of a certified applicator" (162.31 Pesticide Use Classification, Pesticide and Toxic Chemical News, 2 May 1979, pp. 18-22). Some or all formulations or uses of these pesticides are restricted as described.

(6)   *Source:*   questionnaire carried out on behalf of OXFAM by British Agrochemicals Association. Results sent to OXFAM 10 November 1981.

The absence of an asterisk does not necessarily indicate that the pesticide concerned is *not* exported from the UK to the Third World. Some of the pesticides listed were not included in the questionnaire and not all companies responded to the questionnaire. The presence of an asterisk, though, means that such exports do take place.

(7)   The WHO datasheet gives dermal LD_{50}s of 60 (female rat) and 90 (male rat) but the WHO classification of pesticides by hazard gives a dermal LD_{50} of 10.

(8)   *Source:*   Dr. Dwight B. Culver, "Toxicology of Pesticides" in *Report on Seminar, Workshop and Training in Pesticide Management,* Indonesia, 1974 UC/AID p. 130.

(9)   Dermal LD_{50} to "laboratory animals unspecified" (Source USAID, op.cit.)

(10)   As seed dressing.

Appendix II

UK PESTICIDE EXPORT STATISTICS

Table I

Export (fob) of Formulated Pesticides etc.

	£ thousand	
	1979	1980
Insecticides, fungicides, disinfectants, herbicides and similar preparations:		
Preparations based on copper compounds:		
Insecticides and fungicides	3,405	3,519
Herbicides	4,068	2,386
Other	1,243	1,634
Other:		
Disinfectants	13,577	18,219
Insecticides	76,223	78,488
Fungicides	10,118	11,337
Herbicides:		
MCPA; CMPP; 2,4-D; 2,4,5-T; 2,4-DP and their esters and herbicides containing these acids or their esters	21,280	24,146
Other	49,270	51,004
Other	20,713	20,365
Total	199,897	211,098

Source: Business Statistics Office, "Business Monitor", quarterly statistics, PQ279.4, 'Formulated pesticides etc.', Third quarter, 1981, HMSO.

Table 2

UK Pesticide Exports, 1980 ("Disinfectants, Insecticides, Fungicides, etc.") In Value Order.

Rank	Country	Total kg.	Value (£)
1	France	9,676,589	17,210,105
2	Nigeria	15,346,062	16,949,456
3	USA	4,630,567	13,046,555
4	Netherlands	4,831,641	9,810,001
5	Egypt	2,284,076	9,252,367
6	Fed. Rep. Germany	5,355,904	9,082,067
7	Irish Republic	8,291,986	8,907,037
8	Saudi Arabia	5,218,025	8,847,633
9	South Africa	4,192,921	6,833,678
10	Canada	3,202,984	6,174,162
11	Belgium-Luxembourg	4,368,748	6,013,848

12	Japan	2,000,237	5,020,817
13	Libya	7,728,703	4,861,195
14	Spain	1,983,916	4,172,714
15	Italy	2,934,397	4,133,314
16	Sweden	3,790,910	3,658,337
17	Denmark	2,725,274	3,456,586
18	Sudan	1,818,697	3,398,754
19	Thailand	2,976,158	3,017,896
20	Syria	1,110,741	3,000,727
21	Cuba	1,768,829	2,979,780
22	Israel	774,843	2,575,294
23	Iraq	876,421	2,304,485
24	Switzerland	540,251	2,008,924
25	Australia	836,002	2,002,996
26	Abu Dhabi	1,343,510	1,998,031
27	Turkey	492,215	1,917,588
28	Iran	1,627,899	1,900,796
29	N. Yemen	856,708	1,625,409
30	Algeria	247,429	1,544,368
31	Greece	871,868	1,458,783
32	Norway	1,137,885	1,294,455
33	Malaysia	756,299	1,270,553
34	Yugoslavia	661,266	1,268,708
35	Dubai	1,016,421	1,222,634
36	Poland	371,677	1,193,392
37	Austria	531,761	1,140,223
38	Lebanon	910,505	1,088,114
39	Argentina	237,843	1,086,014
40	Indonesia	468,251	1,058,357
41	Portugal	735,004	1,039,322
42	Kuwait	813,401	989,957
43	Finland	1,602,196	975,713
44	Bulgaria	420,022	974,486
45	Brazil	311,788	960,865
46	Philippines	942,451	935,266
47	New Zealand	504,165	912,642
48	Kenya	513,652	850,908
49	Romania	268,316	829,028
50	Barbados	443,749	811,725
51	German Democractic Rep.	175,980	798,035
52	Jordan	699,735	786,206
53	Morocco	228,039	781,071
54	Dominican Rep.	327,227	761,327
55	Hong Kong	842,972	733,916
56	Czechoslovakia	166,907	722,939
57	Oman	581,292	716,593
58	Hungary	109,876	695,075
59	Taiwan	258,217	681,433
60	Singapore	737,876	681,024
61	Soviet Union	338,505	574,821
62	Qatar	466,235	574,791
63	Tanzania	390,503	561,905
64	South Korea	85,295	557,217
65	Trinidad & Tobago	392,219	554,779
66	Ghana	407,727	524,518
67	Cyprus	299,512	443,263
68	Ethiopia	385,045	416,243
69	Peru	193,198	412,670
70	Bahrain	249,141	391,788
71	Pakistan	168,155	389,427
72	Malta	371,530	388,826
73	Ecuador	215,308	385,754
74	Dominica	240,251	371,106
75	Papua New Guinea	254,063	347,387
76	Gambia	237,609	333,041
77	India	135,861	331,756
78	Ivory Coast	116,253	311,824

79	Surinam	218,994	288,335
80	Uruguay	66,771	284,850
81	Guyana	165,177	282,819
82	Mozambique	121,940	279,154
83	S. Yemen	219,326	250,921
84	Chile	130,497	243,663
85	Mexico	33,213	237,661
86	Zambia	43,690	232,810
87	Mauritius	131,763	226,274
88	Angola	100,900	215,342
89	Sierra Leone	171,747	180,547
90	Guatemala	143,363	180,169
91	Cameroon	114,665	177,771
92	Colombia	55,427	173,190
93	El Salvador	132,189	170,379
94	Costa Rica	99,626	168,467
95	Zaire	154,137	163,583
96	Bangladesh	107,124	158,654
97	Venezuela	31,357	153,705
98	Curacao	107,666	148,351
99	Bahamas	114,005	147,525
100	Aruba	74,279	142,466
101	Liberia	117,889	131,784
102	Jamaica	76,382	131,303
103	Fiji	66,251	130,638
104	Sharjah	99,001	113,399
105	Panama	86,745	112,050
106	Antigua	71,730	97,722
107	Panama Canal Zone	25,878	93,847
108	Nicaragua	102,122	90,944
109	Zimbabwe	2,422	82,405
110	Martinique	38,442	80,203
111	Sri Lanka	45,320	78,154
112	Paraguay	61,972	74,004
113	Iceland	59,817	70,670
114	Honduras	46,386	68,225
115	Namibia	36,455	68,178
116	Bolivia	20,086	67,779
117	Guadeloupe	36,640	61,657
118	Belize	41,671	59,918
119	Bermuda	56,518	57,956
120	St. Lucia	39,651	47,657
121	Seychelles	30,300	46,300
122	Canary Islands	16,921	45,183
123	Senegal	17,229	44,309
124	Grenada	25,882	40,618
125	Burma	34,590	38,439
126	Benin	18,198	33,455
127	St. Kitts	21,892	33,300
128	Gibraltar	26,701	28,578
129	Malawi	23,139	22,682
130	Gabon	21,000	19,339
131	St. Vincent	11,925	17,973
132	Madagascar	12,107	16,505
133	Tunisia	3,382	15,160
134	Somalia	7,968	13,564
135	China	7,632	13,201
136	Togo	9,606	12,835
137	Montserrat	7,197	12,659
138	Upper Volta	8,335	12,338
139	Brunei	13,298	11,761
140	Haiti	8,172	9,718
141	Comoros	9,878	7,933
142	St. Helena	3,848	7,777
143	US Virgin Is.	5,252	7,708
144	Puerto Rico	4,424	7,076
145	Brit. Virgin Is.	6,030	6,937

146	Sao Tome-Principe	5,531	5,850
147	Cayman Is.	4,262	5,754
148	Guinea	2,512	5,504
149	Faroe Islands	5,600	4,840
150	Djibouti	3,157	4,596
151	Western Samoa	3,940	4,517
152	Tonga	3,848	4,488
153	Cape Verde	4,093	3,078
154	New Caledonia	1,693	2,703
155	New Hebrides	2,120	2,561
156	Solomon Is.	2,488	1,858
157	Rwanda	1,690	1,789
158	Falkland Is.	709	1,381
159	Nepal	725	1,030
160	Niger	4,990	925
161	Congo	1,008	925
162	Mauritania	182	880
163	St. Pierre-M'ique	420	514
164	Andorra	150	469
165	Ceuta & Melilla	319	468
166	Albania	52	225
	TOTAL	130,509,393	211,099,638

Source: H.M. Customs and Excise, Statistical Office

N.B. 'Disinfectants' includes sheep and cattle dips and dressings for agricultural use as well as household disinfectants. These are included in all the statistics used in this appendix and, in 1980, made up 19.1% of the total volume and 8.6% of the total value.

Table 3

Proportion of UK Pesticide Exports to Developing Countries,
by Volume and Value 1975-79

Year	World		Developing Countries		% to Developing Countries	
	Tonnes	£,'000	Tonnes	£,'000	Volume	Value
1975	83,658	86,030	37,242	29,674	44.5	34.5
1976	80,003	95,877	37,644	39,729	47.1	41.4
1977	109,768	147,065	51,193	61,081	46.6	41.5
1978	131,387	173,651	62,449	73,671	47.5	42.4
1979	134,601	199,897	66,008	92,387	49.0	46.2

Source: UN Commodity Trade Statistics. Figures are converted from US dollars to pounds sterling at the rates necessary to produce figures consistent with UK export statistics (Business Monitor PQ279.4). These rates are as follows:
1975: 2.2142508
1976: 1.7881035
1977: 1.7459014
1978: 1.9158311
1979: 2.1266352

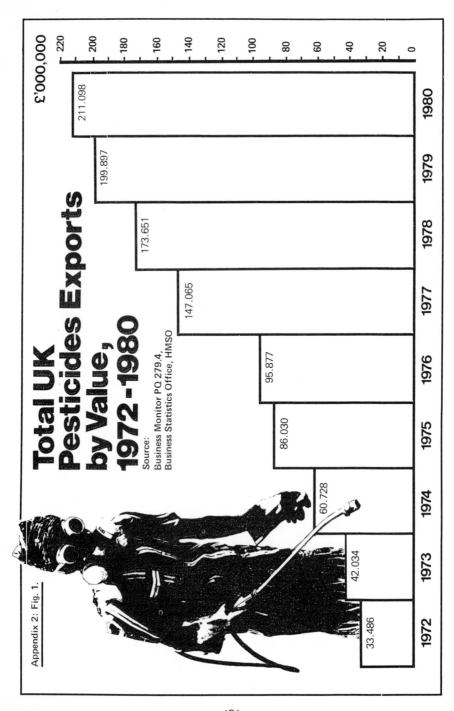

£'000,000

Total UK Pesticides Exports by Value, 1972-1980

Source:
Business Monitor PQ 279.4,
Business Statistics Office, HMSO

Appendix 2: Fig. 1.

Year	Value
1980	211.098
1979	199.897
1978	173.651
1977	147.065
1976	95.877
1975	86.030
1974	60.728
1973	42.034
1972	33.486

Appendix III

MAIN ABBREVIATIONS

EEC	European Economic Community
EIS	Environmental Impact Statement
EPA	Environmental Protection Agency (USA)
FAO	Food and Agriculture Organisation
FIFRA	Federal Insecticide Fungicide and Rodenticide Act (USA)
FPA	Fertilizer and Pesticide Authority (Philippines)
H&S	Health and Safety (specifically the UK Health and Safety (Agriculture) (Poisonous Substances) Regulations, 1975)
HYV	High-Yielding Variety
ICAITI	Central American Research Institute for Industry
ICC	International Chamber of Commerce
ICRISAT	International Crops Research Institute for the Semi-Arid Tropics
ILO	International Labour Organisation
IPM	Integrated Pest Management
IRPTC	International Register of Potentially Toxic Chemicals
IRRI	International Rice Research Institute
LD_{50}	Lethal Dose 50%
MARDI	Malaysian Agricultural Research and Development Institute
OC	Organochlorine
ODA	Overseas Development Administration (UK)
OECD	Organisation for Economic Co-operation and Development
OP	Organophosphate
ppm	parts per million
PSPS	Pesticides Safety Precautions Scheme
R&D	Research and Development
UC/AID	University of California/US Agency for International Development Pest Management and Related Environmental Protection Project (now the Consortium for International Crop Protection)
ULV	Ultra Low Volume
UNEP	United Nations Environment Programme
UNRISD	United Nations Research Institute for Social Development
USAID	United States Agency for International Development
WHO	World Health Organisation

AGAINST THE GRAIN

THE DILEMMA OF PROJECT FOOD AID by Tony Jackson

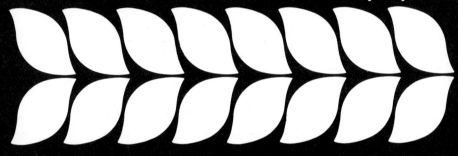

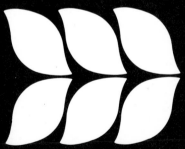

The idea of the rich sharing their food with the poor is persuasive and powerful. But Tony Jackson shows that food aid is an ineffective, even damaging, form of assistance. It is unsuited to stimulating independent and self-supporting growth. It competes with local crops for customers and handling and storage facilities. Because of its bulk it is difficult and expensive to administer. As it is free, it is often treated casually: nothing falls off the back of a lorry more easily than a bag of food aid. Efforts to distribute large tonnages of food result in inadequate attention to project design. Often it does not reach those in need and actually does more harm than good.

For years the food given to Third World countries to help in their development has made little impact. Yet belief in the effectiveness of food aid as a tool for development has gone virtually unchallenged. Mother and child feeding programmes, food for work projects and school food handouts continue apace.

In major disasters, where food aid is essential, it frequently does not arrive in time.

Tony Jackson draws his evidence from his own work in disaster relief in Guatemala and the Caribbean, from the experiences of OXFAM field workers and other agencies, and from official documents. He argues that project food aid should be substantially reduced and administration of what remains vastly improved.

Against the Grain deals with food aid from both Europe and North America. It raises many points to concern the general reader on development issues, and will be of particular interest to those who make aid policy, field workers who carry it out, and journalists and others who follow Third World affairs. It should be required reading on college and university development courses.

Published May 1982 / **136** pages / Cost £**4.50** (plus 40p p & p in the UK).

Against the Grain is distributed for OXFAM by **Third World Publications, 151 Stratford Road, Birmingham, B11 1RD, United Kingdom.** All trade enquiries should be addressed to them.

For individual orders please complete the form below:

To OXFAM, 274 Banbury Road, Oxford, OX2 7DZ, UK.

Please send

. . . . copies of **Against the Grain** at £ . . . . . . each plus postage/packing*

to: PLEASE USE CAPITAL LETTERS

Name . . . .

Address . . . .

. . . .

. . . .

I enclose a remittance of £ . . . .

Postage/packing: 40p in UK. Abroad: 50p surface mail; £1 airmail to Europe, £1.90 elsewhere.

bitter pills

Medicines and the Third World poor
by DIANNA MELROSE

OXFAM

As you read this, millions of people in the Third World are suffering from illness which could be prevented, treated and sometimes cured by medicines developed decades ago. Why don't they get the medicines they need?

- basic life-saving drugs often sell at high prices - 20 tablets of an antibacterial drug may cost as much as the basic diet of a family of four over 2 weeks.

- medicines are produced and sold for profit, - up to a third of the market in some countries consists of vitamins and tonics. Poor people may go without food to buy these unnecessary drugs.

Bitter Pills investigates the alarming facts from the perspective of the poor. It documents the abuses caused by weak controls and reveals that some manufacturers even in Britain are not as scrupulous as they should be in the information supplied to Third World prescribers and patients. Can any of us afford to be complacent when anabolic steroids are promoted as appetite stimulants for malnourished children? Or when antibiotics are sold on market stalls like loose sweets, making drug-resistant disease a certainty?

Bitter Pills describes some of the positive initiatives taken at local, national and international levels to rationalise the use of drugs as part of a broader strategy for better health. It highlights the obstacles to change and concludes with a series of practical suggestions on what can be done in future by government and non-governmental and UN agencies.

The Report is enlivened with real-life stories and illustrations from Oxfam's files. It contains a wealth of unpublished material from the Third World. It is vital reading for all concerned with the fifteen hundred million people in the world who are very poor.

Bitter Pills - medicines and the Third World poor, by Dianna Melrose. Publication September 1982, £4.95 (plus p&p*).

Bitter Pills is published by Oxfam and distributed by
Third World Publications
151 Stratford Road
Birmingham B11 1RD, UK.   All Trade enquiries should be addressed to TWP.

For individual orders please complete this form:

TO: OXFAM
    274 Banbury Road,
    Oxford, OX2 7DZ,
    U.K.

PLEASE USE CAPITAL LETTERS

Please send .... copies of Bitter Pills
to:

NAME ....

ADDRESS ....

....

....

I ENCLOSE REMITTANCE AS FOLLOWS:

.... copies @ £4.95   ....

*Plus Postage & Packing
(per copy postage cost
       in brackets)

United Kingdom (50p)   ....

Abroad: Surface Mail(55p) ....

        Airmail Europe(£1.45)......

    Airmail elsewhere(£2.80) ......

                    TOTAL: ========